W9-AWN-459

GYPSY FOLK-TALES

Selected by Dora E. Yates

BARNES
&NOBLE
BOOKS
NEW YORK

To the memory of

JOHN SAMPSON

in whose gay company I have listened
to and recorded divers folk-tales and legends
from the lips of Welsh, Rumanian and German Gypsies

Originally published in 1948.

This edition published by Barnes & Noble, Inc.

1995 Barnes & Noble Books

ISBN 1-56619-866-6

Printed and bound in the United States of America

M 9 8 7 6 5 4 3 2 1

CONTENTS

CONTENTS

SECTION TWO

Tales told in the vernacular by Gypsy narrators

FOREWORD

The compiler of this book of Folk-Tales is the Honorary Secretary of The Gypsy Lore Society, a scholarly and idealistic body which has existed for more than fifty years and with two breaks has issued throughout that time an erudite but most entertaining quarterly called *The Journal of the Gypsy Lore Society*. Though I have been interested in Gypsies all my life and have been writing about them at intervals for twelve years or more, it was only recently that I discovered that this bravely devoted group of scholars has existed and worked continuously since the Society was founded in 1888.

For in Great Britain the Gypsy has been so absurdly romanticized on the one hand, and so spitefully abused (and in the past persecuted) on the other, that few people have been able to view him objectively, fewer still have tried to understand him, and the merest handful have honestly studied his origins, his language, his traditions, his history.

The sentimental attitude is the commonest, and the first vociferous lover of the Romanies in England, George Borrow, has unhappily been responsible for much of it. There *is*, of course, something romantic about an Asiatic people following their nomadic way of life over the English countryside for the last five hundred years. There *are* mysteries. There are, if you prefer the fashionable word, thrills in following the Romanies either from village to village, or back through time to their obscure beginnings. But the romance and the thrills must be founded on a sense of truth and loyalty, and not depend for their appeal on the artificial or the exotic. It was on the latter which Borrow so often dwelt and in modern times there have been plenty of sentimentalists more culpable than he, men and women who have served their own advantage by pandering to trashy notions of the Gypsy as one of the lost tribes, as a man gifted with second sight whose knowledge of the occult is derived from his ancient Egyptian forebears, as an amorous, shiftless, handsome creature liable to seduce the lady of the manor or break into song with a voice of overpowering beauty, or as a devout pantheist whose rites go back beyond time.

The opposing attitude to the Gypsy is less irritating because it is not so wholly without truth, and its errors are those of thoughtlessness not of the mentally pretentious. According to this the Gypsy is a mere poacher, a worthless vagabond who lives idly off the land which the more industrious house-dweller must till. This is a view frequently held by farmers, particularly those who have none of the seasonal crops for which timely casual labour is essential. The Kentish hop-grower, the Worcestershire fruit-farmer, knows the value of the Romanies who collect in their thousands to do the essential piece-work of harvest-time for which local labour is insufficient.

To the Romani *rai*, the house-dweller who really cares for the people of this strange and interesting race, the Gypsy has little in common with either of these conceptions. He is not the sickly creation of the poetically fanciful, he is not a low-bred thief. He is a very human, very natural oriental who has spent the last five centuries in Europe and in the last fifty years has lost much of his language, superstitions and characteristics, though he delightfully retains enough of them to surprise us every now and again.

However, it is not of the Gypsy that I want to speak here, for the Gypsy speaks for himself in the pages that follow, but of those students of the Gypsy, among whom the compiler of this book must be counted, students whose work has made possible this polyglot collection, the great Romani *rais* of the past, and a few of the present, some of whom have given the best part of a lifetime to research in this quiet field.

Many of their names are little known except to their fellow *rais*, for they received none of the commonplace awards for such labour as theirs. They never used their esoteric knowledge—as they could so easily have done—to impress or intrigue the public, they never played up the Gypsy as a spectacle or a phenomenon, they never, in a word, cashed in on the subject of their researches. They were concerned with the Gypsy himself, and not the world's opinion of him. They realized that to be accepted in Little Egypt, to meet all the demands made of them, was a life's work in itself— to become 'private secretary, legal, medical, and spiritual adviser, general arbiter and tobacco jar' to even one tribe of Gypsies was no trivial matter. And they were frankly not interested in the popular conception of Gypsies. They wanted to know, and not to natter about, the Dark Race.

Not that they went unrewarded in a richer sense. The slightest acquaintance with their work will show that. For once caught by the strange appeal of the Gypsy, illiterate yet knowledgeable, secretive yet impulsively generous of confidence, evasive yet loyal, restless yet constant in friendship, once learning the way through the tent-flap, these men, these studious and respected gentlemen, found that they need never be lonely or bored—need never, for the matter of that, be shelterless or hungry. Several of them died with Gypsy faces round the bedside. For all of them the Gypsy added salt to a life which might have been monotonous.

They had their reward. And they have done their work. If the results of their studies are generally unknown, if the Gypsy is still believed to be a musical descendant of the Pharaohs, a subject for romantic novels and musical films, it is because people prefer this sentimental convention to the truth, and for the Gypsy's sake it is perhaps as well, since fortune-telling is still a flourishing branch of the family business and owes its success to this sort of credulity. But these fifty years of patient research have produced results. The great *rais* have not only cut away the driftwood and destroyed much of the nonsense of which scholars as well as novelists had been guilty, but established a few certainties. The history of the race is still obscure in places, but at least we know beyond doubt from what part of the world the Gypsies came and at what period, we know the origin of their language, we know when they crossed to England, we know how they have been persecuted here and in Scotland, and we know, perhaps most important of all, how they live to-day.

Who, then, are these *rais*? Borrow, first, for all his excitable intolerance. And then that shrewd American, Charles Godfrey Leland, whose own *Memoirs* tell a curious story but whose biography by his niece, Elizabeth Robins Pennell, is even stranger. His *English Gipsies and their Language* is still a classic, and his somewhat bizarre folio *Gypsy Sorcery and Fortune Telling*, illustrated by himself, is full of abstruse and curious knowledge, and written with astonishing gusto though he was nearing seventy when he published it. Theodore Watts-Dunton whose fame unfairly rests on his devotion to Swinburne rather than on his own achievement—that highly-coloured patchwork of a novel, *Aylwin*. It is too garishly lit, and too noisy, perhaps, but what vitality it has, and how readable it is, even to-day and even for someone who has no interest in the Gypsies who play so large a part in it.

Then that little-known man of genius whose books, through some blind spot among publishers, have never been reprinted— Francis Hindes Groome. His *In Gipsy Tents* is a bookseller's rarity and for once deserves its high price for it is as good as the best of Borrow. The compiler of the present collection would, I feel sure, ask nothing better for this book than that it should be considered a worthy successor to *Gypsy Folk-Tales*, the fine assembly which Groome published in 1899. His Introduction to it gives perhaps the best summary ever made of all that is known of the history of Gypsies in Europe. But of all his books I like best his novel which was published in 1896 under the unfortunate title of *Kriegspiel: The War-Game*. It is one of the very few novels in any language which do justice to the Romanies, but it is not for that reason alone that I regret the oblivion into which it has fallen, but because it is in any case a book of enduring significance. A story as grim as *Jude the Obscure* and tempestuous as *Wuthering Heights* it rides gloriously across the English landscape to its gentle conclusion 'on the high green hills which separate England from Wales'.

To be remembered, too, is Henry Thomas Crofton who, as long ago as 1874, collaborated with Dr Bath Smart in producing what is still the best work on Anglo-Romani, *The Dialect of the English Gypsies*. And John Sampson who was Librarian of Liverpool University for thirty-six years and worked for over thirty of them to produce his historic *Dialect of the Gypsies of Wales*, and amused himself by making an excellent Gypsy anthology, *The Wind on the Heath*.

There are other names, unknown beyond the confines of Little Egypt. David MacRitchie and, of a younger generation, Scott Macfie, a Liverpool sugar refiner who devoted the best part of his life to the study of Gypsies, Gilliat-Smith, George Hall, E. O. Winstedt, T. W. Thompson, Archdeacon Ackerley, Sir George Grierson, Dora Yates. Their work on this subject has been published in *The Journal of the Gypsy Lore Society* (which has less than two hundred individual subscribers) and so is known only to fellow devotees of a subject which has never become a cult, a study which has avoided philosophy, a pursuit which has not stooped to affectation.

Finally I would point out that however accomplished and verbose the Gypsy has grown in popular conception, there is one quality of his which is rarely mentioned by Gypsy broadcasters and scenario-writers—his native gift as a story-teller. Yet those who know him best have long realized that though one of his shyest this is perhaps his most enchanting quality. Round any Gypsy fire there are stories told, and the smallest incident of the day is clothed in curious words, tricked out in antiquated or slangy phrases, while here and there, not found easily among the *didikais* of to-day, are men and women who justify Leland's term for Gypsies, the 'Colporteurs of Folk-lore'. And I leave you to judge whether the Romani knows how to tell a tale.

RUPERT CROFT-COOKE

INTRODUCTION

It is now almost half a century since Francis Hindes Groome published his *Gypsy Folk-Tales* and revealed to the world an 'ocean of story' whose depths had hitherto been unplumbed. Inspired by his enthusiasm, and the influence of the Gypsy Lore Society, a new band of Romany Ryes and Rawnies arose, who began patiently to record stories from Gypsies in every country of Europe and thus to supplement Groome's achievement by a vast new store of treasure.

The aim of this book, therefore, is to offer to the general reader a short representative collection of the Gypsy Folk-Tales which these men have gathered. The work has been divided into two sections to differentiate between the tales told in Romani and translated into English by various collectors, and those told in the vernacular by British Gypsies. In both sections the stories have been arranged according to their provenance, and readers who, like the Gypsies themselves, may care to wander from one country to another will find that each group varies in character and style from the next and bears the individual stamp of the respective story-teller.

In estimating the worth of Romani folk-tales it should never be forgotten that every one of them was originally TOLD, and not written, by an expert raconteur, who by his flashing eye and dramatic gestures could convey more to his audience than by a whole line of printed type. Necessarily something of this glamour will disappear when a story is written down instead of being related to a live circle of eager listeners. Much too is lost in translation, for an English rendering often fails to reflect the dignity and severe simplicity of the original tongue, and to reproduce in an uninflected vernacular the narrative style peculiar to most Gypsy idioms in Europe: a succession of short crisp sentences

I

each consisting sometimes of but a single word strongly accented.

Gypsy story-tellers all over the world regard this business of oral transmission very seriously, and the form of their tales is scarcely less fixed than the text of Holy Writ. It has definite openings, links and tags as stereotyped as our familiar English 'Once upon a time' or 'They all lived happily ever after'. The Gypsy audience seems to know the story almost as well as the story-teller himself, and the recital of such a tale is a most dramatic occasion. I shall never forget the experience once at Blackpool of listening to the recital of a German Gypsy tale, where the original narrator would stop suddenly, and one Romanichal after another in his audience would take up the story and continue it in precisely the same style at the point where the previous speaker had left off, while the whole circle echoed the last words of a sentence in chorus. And woe betide the rash listener—be he Gypsy or gentile —who dared to interrupt the thread of the tale, by suggesting a different word, expression or episode from those used by the raconteur! Indeed it would appear that the actual words of the folk-tale are sacred and unchanged from generation to generation, so that in listening to one of these *paramisha* we collectors seem to hear the voices of Gypsies dead long ago. None the less, as will appear from what follows, each Gypsy raconteur will embroider the stuff of his folk-tale in his own fashion and, for better or for worse, impresses on it the indelible mark of his own artistry.

This is especially true of Welsh Gypsy tales which in the present work constitute the first of my groups. They were collected by the great Gypsy scholar, John Sampson, whom Groome describes as 'the Romani Grimm, an ideal collector who possessed the rare gift of being able to take down a story in the very words, the very accents even of its teller'. From the Gypsies of Wales he recorded over fifty tales which had been handed down through the ages from grandam to grandchild. Originally the story had been related by some ancient story-teller of the race of Abram Wood, beside a camp-fire or in a barn in the heart of Wales, to a company of Gypsy men, women, and children who would listen breathlessly to a recital which often lasted the whole night through. But it was from Matthew Wood, who inherited this priceless treasure from his grandmother, 'Black Ellen', that Dr Sampson gathered the bulk of his tales. In his prime the Gypsy Matthew, a romantic figure with mystical deep-set eyes, aquiline nose, sensitive mouth, and long black curls reaching to his shoulders was a prince of story-tellers. In moments of emotion the Romani tale would come tumbling from his lips at a terrific speed almost too fast to be recorded and Matthew, carried away by the drama he was relating, would often identify himself with the hero.

From Wales to Poland is a journey for which the reader requires the 'shoes of swiftness' of a fairy-tale hero, but the stories collected in the neighbourhood of Rabka by Dr Izydor Kopernicki are closer both in style and subject-matter to our Welsh Gypsy group than those of any other country in Europe. Of the thirty tales this indefatigable anthropologist recorded in Romani from John Choron, who was then in prison at Cracow, I have translated three which seemed to me to be typical of the Polish Gypsy raconteur. One of his direct descendants, Milosh Choron, was a Gypsy coppersmith from Cracow.

The number of Gypsy folk-tales which has reached us from Poland's near neighbour, Russia, is lamentably small, partly behaps because the genius of the Tsiganes in that country has expressed itself rather in the art of the celebrated Gypsy Choirs under the Tsarist régime or of the unique and excellent Moscow Gypsy Theatre under the Soviets. So a solitary example must here represent the Russian Gypsy legends which must have been recounted in their hundreds a century ago.

From Tartu, Professor Paul Ariste has sent three Latvian Romani tales which he collected from a Gypsy boy of fifteen, whose skill as a narrator is somewhat crude; but they serve to illustrate an unusual type of story popular among the Nomads of that wild land, whose brand of humour is sometimes spiced with a Rabelaisian flavour.

We next turn to Bulgaria and Yugoslavia, where the Gypsy narrators are highly skilled exponents of their art and enliven their tales with almost every oratorical device known to the professional raconteurs of the East. From the sedentary Gypsies of Sofia, 'those wanderers of classic speech', Mr B. Gilliat-Smith gathered in 1909 a round dozen of stories which it would be hard to surpass from any other collection of Indo-European tales. His narrator Pashi Sulyoff earned his living as a 'hamal' or carrier, and did not aspire to be anything else. In 1909 when his tales were dictated in the 'Erlides' dialect, 'he represented', wrote Mr. Gilliat-Smith, 'a culture which had been stabilized for a long time. He was therefore psychologically, spiritually at peace with himself. He had time to think out his sentences, and their formation came naturally to him.' When the story was good Pashi was as conscious as the recorder that it ranked among the best in the world, and would not be hurried in the telling of it. Indeed his master-piece *The Tale of a God* took three sittings for its completion, 'during which much coffee and many cigarettes were consumed, with the eternal complaint from this typical oriental Gypsy that his elbows were aching, repeated every quarter of an hour'.

In Yugoslavia, also, Professor Rade Uhlik was fortunate in finding an exceptionally intelligent story-teller in Redžo Osmanović, a Gypsy of forty-five years with a profound knowledge of Romani and some facility as a verse-maker. In his view the Bosnian Gypsies are good narrators because they are naturally very talkative, have a retentive memory and unlimited time at their disposal. As they are blessed with a lively temperament and a fertile imagination they are apt to fall into ecstasies over their own narrations and the glow of pride which spreads over the face of a Gypsy raconteur when his tale is read aloud to him is only comparable with the joy of a young author who for the first time sees himself in print. In an entirely different category

4

is the legend with which this section concludes. It was one of many collected from Serbian Gypsies by that great ethnologist and 'beloved physician' Dr Alexander Petrović, who in 1942 was done to death by unknown assailants in a gallant fight against disease and cruelty.

From this important Slavonic group I pass to Hungary, the home of Gypsy music, and here again one must confess that the Tsigane who excels as a fiddler or a cymbalom player in the world-famous Gypsy Orchestras does not shine as a story-teller. The three short legends chosen for this section were collected many years ago by Vladislav Kornel from the Gypsies of Guta, Aranyos, and Almas, and, though 'old-fashioned', exemplify a style of Romani story at one time fairly common in Central Europe.

In Rumania, from the days of Barbu Constantinescu, whose Gypsy tales are considered by many folklorists to be the best in Groome's book, the art of story-telling has always been encouraged among the Tsiganes. And, following in Constantinescu's footsteps, Dr Moses Gaster spent many a laborious holiday in Bucarest recording Romani tales from three ardent Gypsies who used to repeat the stories to him sentence by sentence, and even submitted patiently to a revision and correction of the whole tale for fear the *rai* had chanced to omit some important incident or lively interpolation that had once graced the original version which they had heard from their grandparents. For these Rumanian Gypsy folk-tales are as elaborate in detail as the embroidered clothing of the Rumanian peasant, as anyone can prove for himself if he compare Gaster's version of *The Golden Children*, for instance, with the variants of this widespread story quoted by the commentators of Grimm's *The Three Little Birds* or *The Two Sisters who envied their Cadette* in the *Arabian Nights*.

From western Europe, outside the cycle of Welsh Gypsy stories, my Romani examples are few and far between and include only one Piedmontese tale, recorded from Jeanne Jacqueline Barre, 'une Bohémienne à Cannes', and discovered by Mr E. O. Winstedt in

Bataillard's MS. collection in the Manchester Public Library; one German Gypsy specimen recorded from a band of Sinti who had roamed from Prussia to Blackpool; and an excellent Belgian story heard by M. Jan Yoors as a boy when he was living with a Lowara tribe as the adopted son of its Chief. As a specimen of the narrator's art *The Mosquito* is one of the most original in this collection. In it, the story-teller does not identify himself with his hero, as is the common practice with some Gypsy narrators, but regards that character with critical aloofness and even strong distaste for his behaviour, which he conveys to the audience by typical Romani curses, or apologies for the fellow's offences against the prescribed Gypsy laws of decency.

Let us now, after the manner of our story-teller, leave the Elder Brothers, the Romá of the Continent, and return to the Youngest Brother, the British Romanichal. Scorned by their foreign brethren because they have partly lost their mother-tongue and generally tell their stories in the vernacular, the Gypsies of Britain have nevertheless preserved a precious store of traditional tales, for which the tireless collectors, Dr Sampson, T. W. Thompson, and Andrew McCormick, have angled for months or even years and finally landed with great skill and patience. In the second half of this book, therefore, I have grouped together fifteen of these tales collected in widely-separated districts of England, Wales, and Scotland from such expert story-tellers as the North Country Grays and Locks; from the trilingual Romani *chai* Rosie Griffiths; from the racy South Walian Gypsy, Cornelius Price and from the old Scottish Tinkler woman, Mary McMillan. All these are every bit as good raconteurs as their European cousins, and the breezy idiomatic English in which they told their tales has often miraculously preserved for us a dialect which is fast disappearing.

In the category of British Gypsy tales I have included also one previously printed by Groome, which was related to him partly in colloquial English and partly in Welsh Romani by that inimitable story-teller, John Roberts. The exuberant fancy and pointed Romani allusions of this famous old Welsh Gypsy harper make his stories, which he was able to transcribe himself, unique, so that no book of Gypsy folk-tales could have been representative without a specimen of his incomparable narrative skill.

To complete this section it is also necessary to give a few examples of Lying Tales (Lügenmärchen), a type of story particularly popular among our Romanichals, who to this day rejoice in repeating them with a gusto and a rough humour peculiarly characteristic of English Gypsies. In fact, judging from their number and variety, it may be said that this genre of all others is the one most favoured by the Gypsy narrators of Britain. But as Gus Gray explained to Mr Thompson: 'You see, Rai, us Gypsies is a very polite race o' people an' we don't like to say to a man as he's lying—it's a bit strong to call a man a liar, isn't it now?'—so these stories are generally attributed to such semi-legendary romancers as Appy (Absolom) Boswell and Lander Smith.

After sampling stories from these varied groups the reader will realize that the Indo-European stockpot is common to all genuine folk-tales. Incidents and characters may vary in detail and combination from country to country, but it is precisely by these variations that one can judge the authenticity of a traditional tale. In the main, says Professor Halliday, 'the repertoire of Gypsies appears to conform naturally enough to that of the land of their sojourn', and so we find that the *peris* of the *Arabian Nights* may masquerade as 'little men and little women beautifully dressed in the old-fashioned style' in Welsh Gypsy folk-tales, while the Evil Genie appears as a 'Chordilenjis' in Bulgarian, the Vampire as 'Baldhead's Cannibal sister' in Serbian, or 'The Lady in Want of a Husband' in English, and the Supernatural Bride as Ileana Simziana in Rumanian Gypsy stories. But in essentials folk-tale characters and episodes are substantially the same all the world over, and the hero—be he Janik, Yankos, Peter, Baldhead or good old English Jack—is always the Youngest Brother,

7

generally despised as a fool. His virtues are reverence for his mother, generosity in sharing food with strangers and helpfulness to men or animals in distress. For the rest he is cunning and fortunate rather than wise and deserving; and while possessed of courage somewhat of a braggart and liar. In love affairs, in spite of his uncouth manners and slovenly appearance, he is always successful over his rivals though more courted than himself a particularly ardent suitor.

As a rule the Gypsy story-teller cares naught for the morals of his tales, but in his tags sometimes thinks it necessary to vouch for their veracity by pretending that he himself actually saw the incidents described, and has come straight from the scene of action to relate them to his audience. Other narrators, however, point the finger of scorn at fiction as being distinct from truth, and frankly describe the tale they have just told as 'a big lie'—for which none the less they expect as a reward 'a big pudding' or 'a big hedgehog's liver'. It is these homely Gypsy touches, such as the heroine's begging-bag, and the hero's fiddle-carving, and the caravan in the Latvian stories, or the erecting of a tent and collecting bits of half-burnt wood for a fire in the open in the Sofian 'Chordilenjis', that make the narrative convincing. And, if we do find such improprieties as the introduction of conscription into a Polish Gypsy story, if we listen to a call on the telephone in a Bulgarian Gypsy's recital, or hear of a hospital and modern surgery in a Lowari tale, these are not so much anachronisms as a proof that the narrator was both a knowledgeable man himself and one conscious of addressing a company of Romani men and women who were in every way as up-to-date as their gentile neighbours.

From time immemorial members of the Romani race have ever been celebrated as entertainers and in their tales have sought 'to give pleasure to their audience and help to pass away their leisure hours'. It is with this same hope that I offer to the world outside the tents and caravans this collection of Gypsy Folk-Tales.

D.E.Y.

SECTION ONE

TALES TOLD IN ROMANI
AND TRANSLATED INTO ENGLISH

WELSH

Recorded by John Sampson

—————————————⟨≈⟩—————————————

1. The Leaves that Hung but Never Grew

There was a lonely little cottage and a mother and her
daughter living there. They were poor as poor could be, and
the girl was forced to go and look for work.

She set off and she came to a great mansion. The lord
asked her what she wanted; he called her in. 'I am seeking
work.' 'I will give thee work.' The task which he set her was
to find the leaves that hung but never grew.

Away she went to seek them. As she was going down the
lane she met a little dwarf. 'Good day to thee', quoth he. He
turned and looked after her. He went home and told his
wife that he had seen a lovely young woman upon the road
but she was looking troubled.

She journeyed on until she found a small house. Never
before had she seen it: she was astonished. 'This is all strange
to me', she said to herself. She knocked at the door and out
came an old witch. The young girl asked for work, and the
witch bade her come into her little parlour. She saw a great
black boar chained up in one corner. The old witch made
some good tea for her, and gave her plenty to eat. She ate
her bellyful, and made an end of eating.

Now the only work which the old witch had to give her
was to look after this black boar. The girl tended the boar
for weeks. She knew not how to question the old witch concerning the leaves.

She grew weary and discontented. One day she exclaimed
to the black boar: 'O boar, boar, see the state my hands are
in now! They were white and clean when I came here; but
how rough and dirty are they now through looking after
thee!' 'Wait a bit', quoth he, 'and perhaps thou too wilt
presently find thyself a black sow in the other corner! Why

hast thou come hither?' the boar asked her. 'I came here to
seek the leaves that hung but never grew.'

No sooner were the words spoken than the boar was transformed into a young gentleman. 'Go upstairs into the
witch's bed-chamber', quoth he, 'and put thy hand beneath
her pillow. Thou wilt find a little wallet there. When thou
layest thy hand upon the leaves, wish that the witch may
remain asleep and not awaken.'

She went upstairs; she laid her hand upon the wallet, and
willed the witch to remain asleep and not awaken. She took
the wallet and came downstairs, and gave half the leaves to
the young gentleman.

'And now', quoth he, 'let us devise three enchantments for
the witch when she wakes and asks whether thou art coming
to bed. First the poker shall say: "I am raking out the fire."
Then the broom shall say: "I am sweeping the house."
Lastly the chair shall say: "I am coming now." ' The girl
wished these three things, and the two fled away together.

Lo! the witch awakens. She called the girl to come to bed.
The poker answered: 'I am raking out the fire.' She called
her again. The broom answered: 'I am sweeping the house.'
She called her once more. The chair answered: 'I am coming
now.' The girl came not. The witch called yet again. There
was no answer.

The witch was furious. She realized that the two had
escaped. She called her daughter and told her to follow
them, and whatsoever she should see on the road to bring
home with her.

Lo! the two are speeding on their way. They saw the
witch's daughter coming after them like the wind. Now she
has almost overtaken them! Said the gentleman to the
maiden: 'Wish thyself a duck and me a running stream, and
when she tries to catch thee dive beneath the water.' She
did so. The youth was transformed into a running stream
and the girl turned herself into a duck.

And now the witch's daughter overtakes them. She came
up to the duck and tried to catch her. 'Duck, duck, pretty
little duck', quoth she; 'hast thou seen any one pass this way?'
But every time that she came close to the little duck, the little
duck dived beneath the water.

The witch's daughter went home and told her mother that she had seen a little duck swimming on the water and naught besides. 'Those were they!' cried the old witch. 'Do thou return and fetch me but one feather from the duck, and I will very soon have them back again.' She returned to get the feather. She saw neither duck nor stream. Both had vanished. She was broken-hearted. She went home and told the old witch that she could find nothing.

Lo! the two haste away until they reach a cross-road. Here they were obliged to part from one another. They made a pact that he should go to his home and return again to her. Quoth the girl to the youth: 'When thou arrivest home let not any of thy kinsfolk kiss thee, or thou wilt forget me.'

This young man went home. His family had not seen him for years. His brothers and sisters hugged him and kissed him, and he forgot all about this young maiden.

The girl waited a long time at the cross-roads. At last she felt sure that his kinsfolk had kissed him, and that she was forgotten. She went home to her mother, to the humble cottage where she lived.

Two days passed. The lord came to see whether she had found the leaves. 'Thou hast come home, young woman', said he. 'Yes', quoth she, and she put her hand into a box and drew forth the leaves. The lord knew them as soon as he saw them.

Now there was a great reward offered to whomsoever should find these leaves; but this poor girl knew nothing about it. The lord wanted the money for his own daughter. He did not know how to get rid of this poor girl. He invited her to come to the mansion to take tea, and her poor mother expected that she would return home with much money.

Now this lord wanted to take her life. So he lodged her in a fine room with a bed to herself. Above her head was a sort of canopy set with iron spikes which was to fall upon her and kill her while she slept. When this canopy descended it was to make a great noise, so that the lord might know that she was killed.

Lo! it is midnight now. The clock struck the hour. It awoke the girl. She saw this canopy descending closer and closer upon her. She bethought her of the leaves. When she bethought her of the leaves, she bethought her of the young man. She drew a leaf from her pocket, and immediately he stood before her. She sprang up and gave him her hand.

The young man told her to will them all to sleep. She willed them to sleep. 'Now then', quoth he, 'let us be gone.' He went to the door and opened it softly. The two stole away and no one beheld them go. All was still.

'I am afraid to live with my mother', quoth she to him. 'I want to go further away, so that the lord cannot find me.' 'So be it!' said the young gentleman, 'I will come with thee, go where thou wilt.'

He took her to his own home. 'And now', quoth the young gentleman, 'we have a place where we can talk undisturbed. Shall we two wed?' She gave him her hand. 'That is the very thing I myself desire', said the young woman. 'I had it in my mind to ask thee.'

The gentleman told the coachman to harness the horse to the carriage, and they both drove away to London. In London they were married. Then they came back again to Wales. They kept a mill beside the sea and lived there happily from that day to this.

And I deserve a big pudding for telling thee this lie.

2. The King of the Herrings

Somewhere very far away lived a quarryman. He was old, and his wife had never borne him any children. At last a son was born to them, and all the neighbours were amazed—the man and woman were so old to have a child.

The father died and the son took his place. And lo! an old man passes by, and the youth gazed upon him. Now the old man asks him: 'Wilt thou come with me to seek our living?' 'Yes', quoth Jack. 'Then say that thou wishest me turned into an old nag.' 'Done!' quoth Jack. 'Get on my back; let us be off.'

So off they set, the old nag and Jack, along the road. Said the old nag to Jack: 'If thou shouldst chance to see or hear anyone in trouble on the way, go and find out what is the matter, and if thou canst do aught, do it.'

And lo! and behold! here we are upon the road. And here we are taking the hill. And now the pair are well on their way. Quoth Jack to the nag: 'I hear something.' 'Go and see what it is.' Jack got down from the horse's back to see what was there. He saw a little herring that the tide had left stranded. Jack picked it up and put it back in the water. And lo! the fish swam right up to him. Quoth the fish to Jack: 'Whatsoever I can do for thee, call upon me, the King of the Herrings, and I will do it.'

Away they go over the hill. 'Jack, touch nothing that thou seest, even though it be the finest thing thine eyes have ever beheld.' And lo! the wind blew a feather into his mouth. Twice or thrice did he spit it out. Back came the feather again. He thought it a pretty feather, and put it in his pocket.

And now they come to an old castle. And they heard a great uproar within the castle. 'Go and see what is the matter', said the old nag. Jack went up to the castle and knocked at the gate. No one came out to him. He opened the gate and went in to see what was happening. He saw a giant lying on a bed, helpless. He could do nothing for himself: he was ill. There was no maid-servant to give him food. 'What ails thee, friend?' 'I have no serving wench in this place. Go bring me food and a tankard of ale from below.' The giant ate his bellyful, and bade Jack call upon him if ever he could do aught for him.

Now the pair are going downhill. Quoth the old nag: 'What didst thou see on the mountain?' 'I saw nothing but a little feather which the wind blew into my mouth.' 'Didst thou take the feather?' 'Yes, I have it in my pocket.' 'This feather will bring us misfortune; but keep it, do not let it go.'

And now the young man went to a grand mansion to look for work. The master of the house came out to see his craft with the quill. It was excellent: thou couldst not beat it.

Then he went in search of some place to sleep in. The master invited him to sleep in the house. 'Nay,' said Jack, 'I will go to my old nag in the stable.'

Everyone marvelled at his feats with this feather. One day the man-servant said to his master: 'Call him hither, master, that I may get hold of his quill.' The master called him. He came. The servant took away the quill, and put another on the table in its place.

'Master, I have it: the man who brought the feather here can bring the bird too.'

Said Jack to the old nag: 'The master wants the bird.' 'Go, Jack, and ask him to give thee three days and three purses of gold.' They set off in search of the bird. 'Jack, go up to the castle and walk in. Thou wilt see a company feasting at table. Touch nothing. In a corner thou wilt see a draggle-tailed bird in a cage. Go, take it, but tarry not.'

Out he comes to the old nag carrying the bird. The pair returned, bringing the bird with them. Now the master and his servant talked it over as they looked at the bird. The servants said to the master: 'The bird is pretty; the lady is prettier still.' Quoth the servant to his master: 'The man who brought the bird here can bring the lady too.'

Jack went out to the old nag and told him that the master wanted the lady. 'I warned thee about the feather, Jack. Go and ask him for three days and three purses of gold.' Jack went back to ask the master. He got the money and the three days.

And away they go! They talk together on the road. Said the old nag to Jack: 'Jack, do thou wish me turned into a ship upon the sea.' As soon as the word was spoken, there was the ship on the sea.

And here they are going aboard. The ship was laden with silk. Now they are sailing beneath the castle. 'Jack, go up to the castle, and ask to see the lady. She whom thou wilt see coming forth to thee is not the lady: ask to see the lady herself.'

Jack went to the castle. He knocked at the gate, and lo! a lady appears. She was not the mistress; she was the housekeeper. He said to her: 'I want to see the lady herself.' The servant went in to tell her mistress. Anon the lady comes out. Jack told her there was a ship at anchor below the castle, and she stepped down to look at the silk. The lady came aboard, and one of the crew led her to the cabin where the silk was stored. Jack remained on deck. He weighed anchor and the ship sailed away.

And now they are far out to sea. By this time the lady had finished her business and come on deck. When she saw that she had been trapped, she felt in her pocket, pulled out her keys and flung them into the sea. The sea turned red as blood, and was troubled by a mighty storm.

Here they are back at the mansion. Jack led the lady inside. The master and the servant spoke a few words together. Quoth the servant to his master: 'The man who brought the lady here can bring the castle too.'

Jack went out to the old nag and told him. 'Well, Jack, I warned thee about the feather, that it would bring us misfortune. Go back, Jack, and ask him for three days and three sacks of gold.' Jack went back and got them.

When they were both well on their way, the old nag asked Jack: 'What did the giant say to thee?' 'He promised he would do anything for me.' 'Go to him and tell him what thou wantest."

So up Jack goes to the castle. He told the giant what he wanted, and the giant fell a-laughing at him. He sent him out to fetch his chain, but Jack could not lift a single link. Again the giant burst out laughing, and straightway strode out, picked up the chain, and slung it over his shoulder.

Now they both hasten down to the lady's castle. The giant fastened the chain to the castle, put it on his back and carried it down to the lady's biding-place. There was a high wall round the lady's castle and the gate was locked. Quoth the lady to Jack: 'I want my keys. I cannot open the gate.'

Again Jack went out to consult the old nag. 'Jack, I warned thee about the feather. Go back and ask for such and such things.' He went back and got what he wanted.

So here they are again journeying along the road. 'Jack, what did the little fish say to thee?' ' "Whatsoever I can do for thee, I will do: shouldst thou have need of me, thou must call upon the King of the Herrings." '

Jack and the old nag made for the spot where he had found the fish, and hailed him. Lo! the fish swam up to him. Jack told him about the keys. 'I will go in search of them, Jack.' He disappeared and was gone a great while. He came back, but he had not found the keys. 'Jack, I have not found them,

17

I will try again.' And again he was gone a great while. At last he reappeared and he had found the keys, and he gave them to Jack. The herring swam away and the old nag and Jack returned home.

Jack handed the keys to the lady. The lady asked Jack: 'Which wouldst thou rather, Jack, that thy head, or that thy master's head be cut off?' Jack stopped to think what answer he should make. Then he said to the lady: 'Do not slay him, slay me.' Quoth the lady: 'Thou hast answered well, Jack, thou hast answered well. Hadst thou not spoken thus thou wouldst have been slain. Now it is the master who will be slain.'

Jack and the lady were married and the master was slain. And the lady and Jack still live in the castle.

And now thou hast my tale!

3. Frosty

An old man was strolling along the road with his hat cocked on one side. His name was Frosty. He had walked half a mile, when he met another man. This man was lying on his belly with his ear to the ground.

'What art thou doing here, thou fool?' asked Frosty. 'I am no fool. I am listening to the Members of Parliament making speeches in London.' 'Thou wilt be of use, come with me. Thou hast excellent hearing.'

The two walked on down the road. They met another man with a gun on his shoulder. 'What art thou doing there?' 'Dost thou not see what I am doing? There is a fly upon a rock in America: I am going to shoot it.' 'Thou wilt be of use, come with us.'

And the three went on until they met another man. 'What art thou doing there?' asked Frosty. 'There is a mill far away over yonder, and there is no wind: I am blowing the sails round.' 'Thou wilt be of use. Wilt thou come with us?' The man went with them.

They walked along until they met another man carrying one of his legs under his arm. 'Why dost thou do that?' 'I have pulled my leg off lest I should run too fast.' 'Oh, thou must come with us.'

They went on, and presently saw another man carrying a huge tree upon his shoulder: a great powerful man was he.

At last they came to a town. They heard the talk of the King's court—that he had an old witch who was a swift runner, and that a great reward was offered to whatever man could beat her. 'Let us go up to the palace', said Frosty.

They went up to the palace, and Frosty and the King had a parley about the race. 'I have a man who will run with her', said he. The whole band slept in the palace that night.

They arose betimes. This was the morning on which Run-well and the witch were to have their race. They began to run. 'Wait a bit, the old witch is beating him', exclaimed Shoot-well to Frosty. So he shot a dart into her knee, and Run-well beat the witch.

The King was furious at this. 'Who are these men?' said he to himself.

The old witch counselled the King: 'To-morrow, proclaim that thou desirest the lake in front of the palace to be drained dry.' Now the six were sleeping in the palace again that night, and Hear-well overheard this talk. He told Frosty what was going to happen.

They arose betimes. The King came and told them that he wanted the lake drained on the following morning. The day dawned, and out they went, every one of them. Frosty summoned Blow-well. Blow-well blew the lake dry; he blew all the mud and stones out of it and left it bare.

The old King did not know how to deal with them. They had beaten the witch hollow. 'I will lodge them in my old iron chamber and kindle a great fire beneath it until it grows as hot as an oven, and I will burn them to death.' Night fell. The old King summoned the six men, and threw open the door of this chamber. 'Wouldst thou like to sleep here to-night, Frosty?' Frosty entered. 'Yes, we will sleep here; it seems a warm room.' The old King smiled. 'Yes, it is a warm room, and it will be warmer still presently.'

In went Frosty and his men. 'We shall sleep snugly here.' They sat down, and talked a little before settling to sleep. The room grew hotter and hotter. Presently it became too hot to stop in. So Frosty cocked his hat on the other side. The men were chilled to the bone, and began to shiver. When they were half dead with cold, Frosty tilted his hat up a very little. Then the room grew cool, and the six lay down and slept.

The old King came in the morning to look for them. He was amazed to find them alive. He called them outside. 'Go over there and get your breakfast', said he. When they had finished their meal, he returned, and said: 'I want a ship built upon that lake. I want to see it before the door to-morrow morning.'

Morning dawned, and the ship had been built. 'I want the ship to sail with no water beneath it.' Frosty summoned Blow-well. He blew the ship out of sight, until none could see it.

The King asked Frosty: 'How much money dost thou want to be off?' 'As much as one of my servants can carry.' 'Thou shalt have it', quoth the King.

And here comes Strong-man with a huge sack. He opened the mouth of the sack. He half filled it. 'That is as much as thou canst carry', said the King. Strong-man lifted the sack in his hand. 'Dost thou call this trifle heavy? Fill it.' The old King looked angrily at him. He filled the sack. 'I have filled it now: there, take it, and be off, and do ye never come here any more.' They took the gold and departed.

When they had gone the old King was beside himself with grief at the loss of all this treasure. He sent his soldiers after them. Hear-well heard them coming. 'Wait a moment, I hear an army pursuing us.' The men halted and looked behind them. 'Do not fear', said Frosty. The soldiers drew near to them. Frosty cocked his hat on one side. The soldiers were rooted to the spot: they were so benumbed with cold, they could not stir.

Then old Frosty paid off all his men. He went home alone to his native village, and bought a little house for himself.

And there he lives to this day, and is doing well. And the Woods went there and played the fiddle for him.

4. The Crop-tailed Hen

Once upon a time there were two large mansions. In one lived a widow and in the other a widower. The old lady had a daughter and so had the old gentleman. The old lady's daughter was an ill-favoured little creature and a hunchback to boot. As for the old gentleman's daughter, she was a beautiful lady. The widower and the widow married. They all lived together in the old gentleman's house.

The little hunchback had to go down to the well with a pail to fetch water. She took the pail and went down.

There was a cottage near the gate, and a little old woman dwelt there. The old woman was standing at the door, and she invited the hunchbacked girl to come in to have something to eat. The little hunchback grew angry: 'Art thou not ashamed to ask me to enter such a wretched little hovel?' She left her and went down to the well.

She dipped her pail in the well. Three boars' heads rose up. Quoth one: 'Lift me, and wipe me, and comb me, and set me down softly.' She struck them down with the pail. She dipped her pail in the well, and she drew it up again full of muddy water. She went home. 'Why hast thou brought muddy water?' 'I saw nothing but muddy water in the well.'

Now the other girl goes with her pail to the well. She went down the road, and she came to this old woman's cottage. The old woman was standing at the door. 'Wilt thou come in, my lady, and have a mouthful to eat?' 'Yes, that I will,' and in she went. She had something to eat. The old woman gave her a little sweet milk and some bread and butter. Now this old woman was a witch.

The girl left the old woman and came out. She went down to the well. She dipped her pail in the well. Up sprang three boars' heads. Quoth one to the fair lady, 'Lift me, and wipe me, and comb me, and set me down softly.' She lifted him, she wiped him, she combed him, and she set him down softly. She filled her pail with water. The water was clear. She went home with it.

The old woman was bewildered. She knew not what to

make of it. 'How is it that thou canst fetch clear water, whilst thou, daughter, bringest muddy water?'

On the morrow it was the hunchback's turn to fetch water. She set off. She saw the old woman by her door. 'Wilt thou come in, my lady, and have a mouthful to eat?' 'Not I! Art thou not ashamed to ask me?' She went to the well and dipped in her pail. Up sprang the three boars' heads. Quoth the second one, 'Lift me, and wipe me, and comb me, and set me down softly.' She struck them with the pail. She drew a pailful of muddy water and went home. Her mother was furious to see such muddy water again.

Now here is the other girl going to fetch water. Down she went, and she came to the little old woman's cottage. 'Wilt thou come in, my lady, and have something to eat?' 'Yes, that I will.' She went in and had something to eat. She bade the old woman 'Good day', and went down to the well. She dipped her pail in the water. Up sprang the three boars' heads. Quoth one, 'Lift me, and wipe me, and comb me, and set me down softly.' The fair lady did so, filled her pail with clear water, and went home.

The old woman was furious to see the beautiful girl bringing clear water. 'How comes it that yon girl brings clear water whilst my child brings muddy water? I will send them both again to-morrow one after the other.'

The morrow came. Down went the little hunchback. She saw the old witch. 'Wilt thou come in, my lady, to have something to eat?' 'Art thou not ashamed, thou old hag, to ask me to come in?' She went to the well and dipped in her pail. Up sprang the three boars' heads. 'Lift me, and wipe me, and comb me, and set me down softly.' She struck the heads down with her pail.

She turned to go home and saw three fine gentlemen standing before her. Said the eldest brother: 'Here is a grand lady!' 'Yes, brother,' quoth the second. 'What dost thou wish for this lady?' 'I wish that one side of her hair shall be all lice.' He asked the youngest brother: 'And what dost thou wish for this lady?' 'I wish that the other side shall be covered with nits.' Now the eldest brother speaks: 'She is ugly enough now; I wish that she be far more ugly when she reaches home.'

And now the fair lady goes to fetch water. She came to the

little old woman's cottage. 'Wilt thou come in, my lady, to
have a mouthful to eat?' 'Yes, that I will'; and in she went.
She ate and came out. And she reached the well. She dipped
in the pail. Up sprang the three boars' heads. 'Lift me, and
wipe me, and comb me, and set me down softly.' She did so.
The heads sank down. She drew a pailful of clear water. She
turned her head: she saw three young gentlemen. The eldest
brother said to the others, 'Here is a fine lady!' 'Ay, she is a
fine lady indeed.' 'What dost thou wish for this young lady?'
Quoth one, 'I wish that one side of her hair shall be all gold.'
'What dost thou wish, brother?' 'I wish that the other side
shall be all silver.' 'And what is thy wish, brother?' they said
to the eldest. 'She is lovely enough now; I wish that she be
far more lovely when she reaches home.'

And now the two half-sisters are at home. The old lady was
aghast when she saw them—the one so hideous, and the other
so beautiful. It made her ill to look upon them. She took to
her bed and called her husband. 'What shall we do with
these two?' The old man pondered awhile and listened to his
wife before he said a word. 'I know not what to do.' Quoth
the old lady, 'Make a great chest and put them both into it,
and cast them into the sea, and let them go whithersoever
the wind carries them.' It was done, even as the old lady said.

Lo! the two half-sisters are out at sea now. There they have
been for a month. The fair lady found that she was pregnant.
Her time came. She gave birth to a little crop-tailed hen. As
soon as the little hen was born she looked upon her mother,
and she looked upon her ill-favoured aunt. 'Mammy, who is
this ugly creature with thee?'

A week went by. The fair lady found a small penknife in
her pocket. She opened it. She looked at the chest, and cut a
little hole in it with the knife. She thrust her finger through
the opening. She sawed away again to make the hole larger.
She made it larger. Then she put her head through to see
where they were. She saw fields. She went down below and
said to the other girl, 'I have seen fields'. The water grows
shallower and shallower. The wind blew them close up to the
land. There they stopped for a few days until she had made
the hole wide enough for them to creep out of.

They escaped, left the chest behind, and walked up an old

by-lane. They found an empty barn. The little hen went in to see what sort of a place it was. Out she came and told her mother. 'It is all right, there is plenty of straw and the place is dry: come in!'

The three entered. Quoth the little hen to her aunt: 'Go and hide thyself in the straw.' She did so. The little hen heaped straw over her. 'And do thou, my mammy, sit there, I am going to beg food for thee.'

The little hen went up the lane. She found a great hall. She went up to the hall, and knocked at the door. The butler came out to see who was there. He saw the little crop-tailed hen. He took no heed of her; he went in and shut the door.

The little hen knocked at the door again. Out came the butler. Quoth the little hen: 'I want food for my mammy.' The butler went back to his master and mistress. 'A little crop-tailed hen is out there, a-begging for her mother.' The master and mistress rose and came to the door. There was the little hen. 'I want food for my mammy.' So in they went, collected some victuals, and brought them out and fastened them upon the little hen's back.

See! here is the little hen setting off, and now she has reached the barn. 'I have brought food for thee, mammy; give my ugly aunt something to eat, and let her hide herself.' That food lasted the three for three days. Now it was finished. The little hen goes again to the great hall. She got victuals in the same way as she got them before. She brought them home to her mother.

Once more the food came to an end, and her mother told the little hen about it. 'I will find food, mammy.' She went to the great hall. The butler knew what she wanted this time. And the old master and mistress said to each other that they would watch where she went. Away went the little hen with the victuals. 'I have brought food, mammy; give my ugly aunt something to eat, and then let her hide herself.'

Now the old master and mistress followed the little hen this time to watch where she went. They saw her go into the empty barn. They stopped the carriage. They sent the butler to look through the window. He saw a beautiful lady with the little hen beside her, and they were eating. He told his master. His master alighted and went into the barn and spoke with her. He saw nothing of the hunchback; she was hidden in the straw. They took the lady and the little hen into their carriage and drove back to the great hall.

The young master was there. As soon as the lady entered the great hall he gazed upon her; he loved her; he married her. The ugly lady was caught and sent home. The little hen stayed with her mother; no money could buy her.

I was there, and I saw her, and I played the fiddle for them. They paid me handsomely. That is all I have to tell.

5. The Little Cinder-Girl

There was a small house, three daughters, and their mother. The two sisters thought themselves grand ladies, but as for the youngest, they used to hide her in the coal-hole so that no one would see her. They could not bear her, because she was so grimy. They were ashamed to see her about, and whenever anyone visited the house they would say to her: 'Be off, little slut, and hide thyself.'

The two sisters used to go to church. One Sunday after church, they came home, and began to talk about a prince whom they had seen there. The young girl overheard them.

Sunday came round again. The two sisters went to church while the young one stopped at home alone. And a little old woman came to the door a-begging. The young girl bade her enter, and made her some tea. After she had finished the old woman called the girl outside.

There was a white pebble near the door. Said the old woman: 'Take that white pebble and fling it against yonder rock. Thou wilt see a door there; open it, and go in. Thou wilt see a chamber; thou wilt see apparel; thou wilt see a pair of golden slippers. Robe thyself, come out, and pass on to the next room. Thou wilt see a little horse, lead him outside, mount him, and ride to the church. Do not go far within, sit by the door, and let thy horse be tethered near it. Come out before the rest. The young prince will follow thee; he will try to catch thee and to find out who thou art. Hurry home, restore the clothes to the place thou didst take them from, return, and say naught.'

For three weeks the young girl did as the old woman bade her. A grand lady entered the church, and there was nobody there who knew her. Everyone was gazing at her, and the prince fell ill with longing to know who she was. He kept his eyes fixed upon her, and he followed her to see whether he could find out. But she had gone too far for him to discover who she was.

The last week the old woman said to the young girl: 'Mark what thou shalt do now. Do as I bid thee. Go to church, and this time thou must leave still earlier; the prince will follow thee. One slipper will drop from thy foot, and he will come after thee and find it.'

Everything fell out as the old woman had said. The girl returned, put back all her finery, and dressed herself in her old clothes. The two sisters came home and began to talk about the prince. And the young one was listening to them. She asked the two sisters whether she might go to church to see the prince. 'No, thou dirty little slut, go and hide thyself.'

The prince wondered how he could discover the lady. At last he prepared a great banquet and sent a proclamation throughout the land inviting the young ladies to attend. The damsels had no idea what the prince wanted.

The day arrived when the banquet was to be held. And here is the prince in the reception chamber! All the ladies came up to his chair. One lady sat down. The prince took the slipper and tried it on her foot. It did not fit. Out she went. Another lady approached: it did not fit. He tried them all, and there was not one there whom the shoe would fit. The two sisters were there, and the eldest, who was yearning for the prince, chopped a piece off her foot: she would have given her life to get him.

The prince asked: 'Where are all the serving-maids?' One wench entered. She would not do. Then another girl. She would not do. Now the Little Cinder-girl comes in. The prince threw down the slipper. The young girl held out her foot. On went the slipper, and the prince recognized her. The eldest sister would have killed her, if she had not been afraid.

Lo! then there were great preparations for the wedding. The wedding-day arrived. They left the church and returned home. There was a great company of lords and ladies feasting in the castle. At last all was over and the guests departed.

The pair lived together for a year, and the lady was with child. She was put to bed, and bore a daughter. The eldest sister was sent for to come up to the castle to look after her. She brought a puppy up to the lady's room. She took away the babe and left the dog in bed beside her youngest sister. Then she took the child home and gave it to her mother. The prince saw the puppy and was horrified. But he said naught this time.

The lady was with child again. She was put to bed, and bore a son. The eldest sister was sent for to come up to the castle, and look after her sister. Again the eldest sister brought a puppy with her. She put it in the bed and carried off the baby boy. She gave him to her mother. Then she returned to the castle to nurse her sister.

The prince came home. He went up to see his wife. The eldest sister was there. She lifted the blankets and drew forth the puppy. 'Is it not a disgrace for a lady to give birth to a puppy!' The prince spoke no more. He summoned his serving-men: 'Get ye down and make ready to burn her.' His wife implored him to spare her once more. 'If it should happen thus again I will take what comes.' The prince relented: the lady was set free.

A year or two afterwards the lady was with child again. She was put to bed and bore another son. The eldest sister was sent for to come up to the castle. She brought a puppy to the castle, put it in the bed, carried off the child, and sent him to her mother.

The eldest sister was looking after the youngest. The prince came up to see his wife. The eldest sister lifted the blankets, drew forth the puppy and showed it to the prince. 'My God!' he exclaimed, 'what a disgrace for a lady to give birth to a puppy!' The prince leapt to his feet in her bedchamber. 'Where are the men-servants?' They were summoned to drag her out of bed, and carry her down to be burnt.

Lo! the little old woman appears once more! The little old

woman spoke to her. 'Fear not. I am here. Thou shalt have thy children back again, all three.'

The lady was to be burnt. She was carried out of doors. The prince came out of the castle. He paused to consider what he should do. His heart was too tender towards his wife to watch her burn. So he went away, and left her to be burnt by his men-servants.

'Nay,' quoth the lady, 'ye cannot burn me; my dear God is good and he will watch over me.' She kept a stout heart because of what the old woman had said to her. 'Let her go!' said the old woman. She was set free. 'Thou shalt become a young sow in the midst of the forest.' As soon as the word was spoken the lady was transformed into a young sow.

The old woman told the young sow: 'Thou wilt be slain; the prince and his court will hunt thee to death. They will cut out thy liver and hang it beside the gate of the castle. Whoever takes it and repeats certain words will get whatever he desires. Fear not. Thou wilt be restored to life, and wilt regain thy husband and thy children.'

She was in the forest for years, and then the prince's servants found her. They had seen her about for some days. They went home and told their master that there was a sow in the forest they had never seen before. 'We will go and look for her. We will slay her to-morrow.' The sow knew that the nobles and their train were after her. She hid herself.

Let us return to the children. Here are the three alone in the forest; the two sisters had turned them adrift when their grandmother died. The sow found them. She spoke to the children. 'They are hunting me', quoth the sow, 'and mean to slay me.' Saith the mother to her daughter, the eldest child: 'When I am slain, go down to the castle and beg a piece of my liver. Take the piece of liver, and thou wilt get whatever thou desirest. I will return again to you. It was my sister who caused all this trouble.'

They found the sow and slew her. The prince told them to bring her liver to the castle. They took her liver, and it was hung up beside the gate.

The girl went down to the river-side with her two little brothers. They sat down by the river. 'Is not this a pleasant spot?' said the girl to her brother. 'Would it were ours!' quoth

the boy. 'Well, I can get it. I am going down to the castle.'
'Do not stay long, sister.' The girl went to the castle, as the
sow had bidden her; for the sow had told the girl if she desired anything she was to go down to the castle to get a piece
of the liver, and her wish would be granted. She went and
got the liver.

Back she came. 'Now then brother, come here. I will show
thee something. Wouldst thou like a cottage here?' 'I would
indeed, sister.' She told her brother what the sow had said.
As soon as the word was spoken, there stood the cottage.

The three went to live in the cottage. They were there for
years. One day a stranger called to light his pipe and stared
at the three children. He knew not who they were. He went
down to the castle and told the prince about the cottage and
the three children. He told the prince that the three children
were girt with golden belts. The prince offered the man a
reward if he would bring the three belts to him. 'I will go at
once.'

He set off, reached the cottage and knocked at the door.
Out came the sister. The stranger asked for a light for his
pipe. 'Come in', quoth the boy. 'No', said the girl. 'The man
will do no harm, sister, let him enter.'

The stranger came in and asked the younger boy to let
him look at his belt. 'Nay, brother, do not take off thy belt.'
'Sister, the man will do no harm.' The man got the belt. He
next asked the elder boy. 'Nay,' said his sister, 'do not take
off thy belt.' He took it off and gave it to the stranger. He
asked the girl for her belt. 'No,' replied the girl, 'I will never
take off my belt.'

The man went down to the castle and gave the two belts
to the prince. 'I could not get the belt from the maiden, she
would not part with it.'

As soon as the belts had been handed over, the two boys
were turned into swans upon the river. The girl was left all
alone now. Suddenly she remembered what the sow had
told her. In the morning she went down to the castle to get a
piece of the liver, and returned home with it. 'May my two
brothers be restored to their former shapes!' As soon as the
word was spoken she got her two brothers back again.

One day the sister was talking to the elder brother: 'Oh,

brother, if only our mother were with us! We must try to get our mother back.' 'Impossible', said the elder boy; 'no, that is a thing that cannot be done.' 'Indeed,' quoth the girl, 'I will get her back again.'

The girl went down to the river, taking the liver with her. 'I want my mother back again.' Immediately the word was spoken she recovered her mother. The girl fell down in amazement.

Together they went to the cottage and the mother kissed her two sons. 'How didst thou bring me here?' she asked her daughter. 'I will tell thee, mother. A young sow came to me after thou hadst been slain. She told me to go to the castle and get a piece of liver.' 'That is so', agreed her mother. 'Canst thou bring thy father here?' 'Yes,' quoth the girl, 'I will bring him here.' 'When?' asked the mother. The girl went outside. 'Where art thou going?' asked her mother. 'I will return, I am not going far.'

The girl went to the river-side. 'I wish my father to be restored to us.' The word was spoken: there stood her father. He embraced his daughter, and hurried into the cottage. His wife was speechless with amazement. She recovered her senses. Said the prince to his wife: 'Let us go home to the castle!'

'How didst thou contrive to bring me here?' asked her husband. 'I will tell thee. Dost thou remember the liver which hung beside the castle gate?' 'I do', said the prince. 'After I had been slain, our daughter went to the castle to get a small piece of my liver, and when the word was spoken, lo! her wish was granted.'

The prince, his wife, and children went down to the castle. They dwelt there for years, and the children grew up. Then the girl journeyed for a long time in foreign lands in order to see the world. She came home. Her father and mother were overjoyed to see her return. Both the parents died, and the children are living in the castle to this day.

Well! that was all the children had to suffer. There is no more to add. We have reached home with the help of God. And that is the end!

6. The Old Smith

There was an old blacksmith who lived on the hill with his wife and his mother-in-law. And the only work he could do was to make ploughshares. The mother-in-law had an old mare.

Once there came to him a youth on horseback. 'I want thee to shoe my horse.' 'I cannot', quoth the old smith. 'Then give me the tools; I will do it.'

The boy went off and made a great fire. He came out and cut the horse's four legs off. He staunched the blood and put the four legs on the fire. He blew the fire a great while. He took the four legs out of the fire, put them on the anvil, beat them a great while, and threw them down. Then he picked them up, went out, and put them back under the horse.

The old smith was watching him. The youth asked what he had to pay: he gave the smith a golden guinea.

Some days afterwards the smith remembered about his mother-in-law's mare. He wanted her shod. So away he went and brought her to the smithy. He tied her to the door, and cut off the four legs and let them bleed. But he did not know how to staunch the blood. He went in, made a great fire, and put the four legs on the fire. He blew and he blew. Then he went to look for the legs. There was nothing to be seen: he had burnt them all to ashes. He took the old mare and threw her over the hedge.

The mother-in-law and her daughter were always quarrelling. The old smith did not know what to do with them. In a day or two the youth on horseback returned with two old women. 'Canst thou make these two old women young?' he asked. 'No, I cannot.' 'Wilt lend me thy tools? I will do it.' 'Yes, take them.'

The youth got off his horse; he flung down the two old women and bound them. He made a great fire, and put them on the fire. He blew and he blew beneath them. Then he took them outside, set them on the anvil, hammered them well and set them down. They became two young and beautiful ladies. The old smith was watching the youth. The boy gave him a golden guinea.

A few days afterwards it occurred to the smith to do the same with his wife and his mother-in-law. He took the twain, and bound them, and set them on the fire. And he blew and he blew beneath them. Then he went to look for them. There was nothing to be seen: they were burnt to ashes. He flung down the hammer, and went out. 'I have done it now! I have killed my old mare, and I have killed my wife and my mother-in-law.' He scratched his head and knew not what to do.

So he leaves the smithy and sets forth in deep snow and wind, and he had never a hat on his head. The young boy followed him and asked: 'Shall I come with thee?' 'No,' quoth the smith, 'thou hast naught to do with me.' 'Do let me come with thee.' The old smith took him. The boy was barefoot.

The boy talked to him. 'Near by is a great castle, and in it is a mighty lord. He is ill in bed. Let us go there.' 'I can do nothing,' quoth the smith. 'Say naught then: we will go there together, and I will do everything. Tell them that I am thy servant.'

Down they went to the castle and knocked at the door. The butler came out. 'We have come here to heal the great lord.' 'Come in!' He took them in to sit by the fire. He asked them what they would have to eat and drink. They got plenty to eat and drink. The old smith forgot what they had to do. The little boy said to him: 'Now then, when the butler comes in, say that thou wishest to go to the lord.'

They went up to the lord. The young boy called for a knife, a pot, water, and a spoon. He cut off the lord's head and spat on his hands to staunch the blood. He put the head in the pot, and set it on the fire to boil. It boiled a great while. He took a golden spoon and stirred it with the spoon. He took the head out of the pot and put it back on the lord's neck. The lord got well and stood up.

The lord gave them a sack of gold and they set off along the road. 'All that I want', quoth the little boy, 'is new shoes.' 'No, I cannot give thee any: there is little enough for myself', quoth the smith. The little boy went off and left him.

The old smith goes on alone. He met two men on horseback and they seized all his money. The smith journeyed on. He heard about a great castle, and that the lord of that castle was ill.

Up goes the smith to see him. He knocked at the door. The butler called him in and gave him plenty to eat. After he had done eating, the old smith went up to see the lord. He called for a pot and water and a spoon. He cut off the lord's head and let it bleed. But he did not know how to staunch the blood. He put the head in the pot on the fire to boil: it boiled a great while. He took the spoon and stirred it. He could do nothing to it; the head was falling to pieces and the lord was bleeding to death.

Some one came and knocked at the door. The smith was afraid. 'No one must come in here.' 'Wilt thou let the little barefoot boy in?' The old smith hearkened and opened the door, and let the little boy come in.

He walked straight up to the lord and staunched the blood. Then he went to the pot, took a golden spoon and stirred the head. It was a great while before he could get the head together again: it was boiled to rags. He took it out and set it on the lord's neck. The lord sat up. The smith and the little boy went away after getting two sacks of gold.

On the road the boy begged: 'I want shoes.' 'Very well,' said the smith: 'all the money is thine.' The boy said: 'I do not want it: I want shoes.' The boy got his shoes.

The two were walking along the road, and the little boy said: 'There is another great lord who lives near by. This lord has a wizard and no one can beat him. Let us go there. There are three sacks of gold to be won, if we beat him.'

They went up to the door to get speech with the lord. They were given food, and came away. Then they went into an old house, where there was a huge pair of bellows. The lord's wizard blew up half the sea. 'Now it is thy turn, little boy', said the smith. The boy began to blow. He blew up a great fish that drank all the sea. The wizard began to blow again. He blew up corn like rain. The little boy tried and he blew birds that ate up all the corn. The lord's man blew up many rabbits. The little boy tried again and he blew three greyhounds, and the greyhounds ate up the rabbits. He beat the lord's wizard: they got three sacks of gold.

The old smith hardly knew what to do with his money. It

occurred to him to build a new smithy. And he built a few new houses, a workshop, and three inns.

One day he was doing a little work when an old woman came to the door at nightfall to beg for a lodging. 'All right,' quoth the old smith, 'I can give thee a bed for one night. I have no servant-maid, so go into the house, put the kettle on the fire, and make some tea for thyself.' The old woman ate something and went to bed.

In the morning she arose, and the old smith and she had breakfast together. 'I will give thee three wishes—what dost thou desire?' quoth the old woman. The smith said to her: 'I wish that the man who takes my hammer in his hand cannot put it down again until I say so.' He got his wish. 'What is thy second wish?' quoth the old woman. 'Dost thou see that old chair in the corner?' 'Yes', quoth the old woman. 'I wish that the man who seats himself there cannot get up again until I set him free.' 'All right! thou shalt have thy desire.' 'And I wish that the man who gets into my pocket cannot get out again until I let him.' 'All right!' quoth the old woman. She thanked him and went her way.

A few days after, when his money had run low, a man came to the smithy. He asked the smith how he was. 'Very well,' quoth he, 'how art thou?' They talked for some time until at last this man asked the smith whether he would sell himself. The smith considered a little. 'Yes,' quoth he, 'how much money wilt thou give me?' 'I will give thee a sack of gold.' 'Give it me', quoth the smith. 'Thou must come away with me in five years' time: I will return here to fetch thee.' The Evil One departed and the smith went out to the inn to get a drink.

One day he was in the smithy doing a little work, when the Evil One arrived. 'Now thou must come away with me.' 'Very well,' said the smith. 'Wait a moment, take my hammer, and do a little beating on this anvil. I will come back when I have finished this small job.'

The smith took his work home and afterwards went to one of his inns. He did some hard drinking there, came out, and went to the next inn. He had a drop there too and came out.

Lo! the Evil One leaves the forge, hammer in hand, and goes to seek for the smith. He found him in the farthest inn drinking with the gentry. In came the old Devil. The smith stood up. 'What art thou doing with my tools?' he asked. 'Come here', quoth the Devil. 'Remove this thing and I will give thee five years more.' The old smith took the hammer and went home.

The five years passed day by day. Just after they had come to an end the Devil walked into the smithy. 'How art thou?' quoth he to the smith. 'Very well! how art thou?' 'Now thou must come away with me.' 'All right! sit down in that old chair.' The Devil sat down. 'Wait there a moment,' quoth the smith, 'I want to go home with this.'

The smith went off down to the inn. He got half drunk. The old Devil was tired of sitting down. He tried to get up, but could not. At last he walked off with the old chair behind him down to the inn. He asked whether the landlord was in. 'No,' quoth the woman, 'he is not here, he has gone to the next inn.'

The Devil followed him to the second inn, and strode into the parlour. And there he found the smith. He looked at the Devil. 'What is that man doing with my chair?' said he. 'Come here,' quoth the Devil. 'I want a word with thee. Take away this chair, and I will give thee five years more.' The smith dragged away the chair and the Devil departed. The smith returned home.

The five years passed day by day. Lo! the old Devil is back again. There was no one in the workshop: the smith was out drinking. The old Devil went to seek for him. He found him in the parlour. The old Devil sat down beside him, and whispered in his ear. Said the smith: 'I have called for ale. Turn thyself into a pound in my pocket that I may pay for it.' The Devil did so. The old smith drank his fill and went home to bed.

He was just falling asleep when something under his head began to cry out. He got up, came downstairs, went into the smithy, took the pocket, held it on the anvil, seized the hammer and beat it soundly. 'Let me go', quoth the old Devil, 'and I will leave thee alone. I will never trouble thee again if thou wilt let me go now.' The old smith let him go.

Then the smith died, and he went to the Devil's door and knocked. An imp of Satan came out. 'Tell thy father that the smith is here.' The little demon went and told his father. 'Do not let him in,' quoth the old Devil, 'he will kill us all.' 'Here!' quoth the old Devil to his serving-man, 'take this wisp of straw and set fire to it to light him up to my dear God.'

The Devil's servant did so. The old smith went up to my dear God. There he sits playing the harp, and there we shall all see him one day, if we do not go to the Devil instead.

That is all I have to tell now.

POLISH

Recorded by Dr Izydor Kopernicki

---

7. The Little Horse and the Diamond Necklace

There was once a very old farmer who had no wife and lived alone with his seven sons. At one time there was conscription in the country and they came to this old peasant who had seven sons, and enrolled them all. He prepared a supplication stating that he had a big fortune. 'How could I endure', he said, 'to be left all by myself? I am already an old man, and who would cultivate my fields?' No one paid the least attention to the fact that he was old and wealthy. 'That is no concern of ours', said the authorities to him.

The King got to hear that an old farmer had seven sons, and bade them appear before his Royal Highness. He saw that they were very handsome men and made officers of all of them. They remained in the army for ten years, and then all seven youths wanted to flee far away from that King.

The youngest brother, who was rather foolish, said: 'To what place are we going to flee?' 'Here! what business is that of thine? When we do desert, thou wilt come with us.' 'No, my brothers, I won't desert with you, because I am well enough off here; and you too, you are all officers, what more do you want?' Then these six said to their foolish brother: 'We have no more money.' 'Well, I will write a letter to our father, and he will send you plenty of money.' 'Good! so be it.'

This fool sat down and wrote a letter to his father asking him to send seven hundred pieces of money to his sons. The father sent a hundred florins for each one of them. The money arrived. The fool broke the seal and opened the letter. He summoned his six brothers and said: 'Hearken, my brothers, our father has sent us seven hundred florins, a hundred for each of us.' Well, the fool gave each of them his hundred florins and kept a hundred for himself.

But these six brothers would not obey the King's orders as did the fool, who was now promoted to being a superior officer. The other six brothers—pray pardon me—did nothing but run after the girls for entertainment. So they had no money, not even a sou, because of the huge sums they had spent on the girls.

They appear before the King, and the foolish brother sees them approaching. To him they say: 'Our good little brother, we have no longer a sou; if you write to our father asking him to send us some money, then we won't desert.' The fool replies: 'Brothers, for God's sake beware! for if the King gets to hear of your conduct he will commit you to prison.' But hearken! I will give each of you thirty florins. Only restrain yourselves somewhat, so that the King does not get to know, otherwise shame will fall upon you and men will deride you all over the world, a thing which need not happen to you.'

Well, these six hearkened to their youngest brother and promised him not to behave like that any more. 'Good! I will give you money whenever it is necessary, but you must behave yourselves, otherwise you will bring shame upon me and still more upon yourselves.' 'All right, brother, we will not misbehave any more.'

One day this fool went for a stroll, and saw a remarkably fine horse grazing in a meadow. So he discarded his own sorry nag and mounted this beautiful creature. And as soon as he was mounted, the horse seemed wholly content. In one of the fields he caught sight of a diamond necklace lying on the ground. The fool wanted to dismount, but his horse cried to him: 'Master, for God's sake, do not touch that necklace, or thou wilt bring misfortune on me, and even more on thyself.' But the fool paid no attention, dismounted from his horse, picked up the diamond necklace and hid it in his pocket. He remounted his horse and returned to the King.

Now this King had no wife. And this fool showed the string of diamonds to him. 'Hearken', said the King, 'if thou hast found the necklace, thou must find the lady to whom it belongs.'

He was dumbfounded by this order, and went weeping to his horse. The horse asked him why he was crying. 'Because the King, when he saw that I had found the necklace, ordered me to find the lady also to whom it belonged.' The horse answered him: 'Did I not warn thee not to touch the necklace lest it bring great misfortune on me and greater on thyself? But stop crying, all will be well. And get up on my back.'

Well, he mounted his little horse and came to the house of a witch. Then his little horse said to him: 'Thou art about to eat and drink with a witch and afterwards thou wilt sleep with her twelve daughters. When thou hast lain down, beware of falling asleep. Thou wilt be lying on the edge of the bed nearest the table, but thou must take the girl, the one thou meanest to carry off, and put her near the door, and then lay thyself down next to the wall. This witch will arise in the night and want to kill thee, but she will kill all her daughters, whilst thou wilt be left alive.'

Well, he entered the house and the witch gave him food and drink. Then she said to him: 'Wilt thou sleep with my twelve daughters?' 'Gladly.' So he lay down at the edge of the bed, but in the night he put the girl he was going to carry off near the door, and laid himself down next to the wall. This witch came into the room meaning to kill him and, thinking that he was lying next to the table, killed all her eleven daughters, but the twelfth who was lying next to the door escaped.

Then the fool arose from his place in the bed next to the wall, seized the girl and brought her to his little horse. The horse said to him: 'Go and thank the girl's mother for rearing her daughter for thee, and for her necklace that thou didst find in the meadow.' Well, he mounted the horse with his stolen lady behind him and came beneath the windows of the witch's house. 'I thank thee, mother, for rearing so beautiful a daughter for me, and for her necklace that I found in the meadow.' Then this witch jumped out of the window and hurled fire after him, but he took no heed of it, and escaped with his girl, with that witch's daughter.

He returned to the King. 'Didst thou find the girl?' 'I did, Sire.' He presented to his majesty this marvellously beautiful maiden. 'And now I wish to wed thee.' 'Very good, Sire, I will be thy wife. But if the man was clever enough to carry me off from my mother's house, he must bring me my golden hen that lays diamond eggs. If he brings me this hen, then I will marry your Majesty.'

Well, the King sent him to search for this hen. He came to his little horse, who asked: 'Why art thou so sad?' 'Because this lady told me that she has a golden hen that lays diamond eggs, and that if I steal this hen she will wed the King.' 'Be at peace, fear naught; if we stole the girl we can also steal her hen; only mount me.'

They came to the witch's house. 'Thou wilt see', said the horse, 'at the first door a golden pot hanging on a nail, and in this pot is the golden hen. Thou must steal it for me and come back here immediately.' Well, he went, he stole the hen and returned to his little horse. 'Now, go and thank the girl's mother for having guarded for thee the golden hen that lays diamond eggs.' He came beneath the windows of the witch's house. 'I thank thee, mother, for this golden hen thou hast reared for me, and for the diamond eggs she has laid.' The witch looked up: the pot with the golden hen was no longer on its hook. She hurled boiling water after him. Then the fool cried to his little horse: 'Let us flee, for the love of God! for she is scorching me so terribly that I shall have to drop the golden hen.' But by God's grace they succeeded in escaping from this witch.

He returned to the King. 'Hast thou brought the golden hen?' 'I have, Sire.' He shows the hen to his lady. 'Has my officer brought thee what thou didst desire? Is this thine?' 'Yes, mine it is', she answered. (There were ten eggs, but really they were not eggs but young ladies.) 'Well, now I am going to take thee to my couch.' 'Very good, Sire, I will become the King's wife as soon as the man brings me my golden charger.' 'Good!'

The King says to his officer: 'Thou must go for this horse and when thou bringest this golden charger to my lady, then she will become my wife.' The fool comes to his little horse in great distress. 'Why art thou weeping?' asked the horse. 'Because the King has ordered me to steal this golden charger, and if I bring it to his lady then she will wed him.' 'Come, ask no questions and all will be well. If we stole the lady and her golden hen, we can also steal her charger. Only mount me.'

He got up on his back and they came to the witch's house. 'Hearken,' said the little horse, 'thou must dig a ditch for me and thou must bring me six buckets of water, and six tons of salt and six tons of cabbages and throw them into the ditch. This golden charger will pick up my scent, and will drink up the salt and water and will eat up all those cabbages, and then he will fight with me, will this golden charger. And do thou climb this willow-tree, take this wand, and as soon as thou seest that he is attacking me too fiercely spring from thy perch and with thy wand strike him on the nostrils with all thy force. As soon as thou strikest him he will fall down, and then do thou climb on to his back.'

Well, the little horse reached the spot, and the fool prepared for him six tons of salt, six tons of water and six tons of cabbages, and with the wand in his hand he perched himself on the willow-tree. The golden charger scented the little horse, galloped up, ate all the salt, drank all the water and devoured the six tons of cabbage and began a combat with him. When the fool saw that the charger was pressing his horse too fiercely, he sprang down from the willow-tree and with his wand struck the nose of this steed with all his force. The golden charger fell down and in that instant the fool climbed on to his back. 'And now', said the little horse, 'go and thank the witch.' So he came to her window and said: 'I thank thee, mother, for this golden charger, for the last time, for I shall not return since there is nothing more to take.' The witch jumped out of the window and looked around: the golden charger was there no longer. (He was her son.) From her mouth she vomited flames of fire on the fool, to make him release the golden charger, but he paid no heed, and with the grace of God escaped.

He returned to the King. 'Hast thou brought the golden charger?' 'Yes, Sire, I have.' Well, he presents it to his lady. 'Is this thy golden charger?' 'Yes, Sire, he is.' 'Then, I will take thee to my couch at once.' 'Very good, Sire, I will become thy wife.'

Then this princess ordered them to milk a hundred cows, and to boil the milk in a huge cauldron, and she said to the King: 'When this milk is boiling fiercely, let this officer bathe himself in it, and then I will become thy wife.' Well, they milked a hundred cows, emptied the milk into a cauldron, and it began to boil fiercely.

The fool came to his little horse, who said to him: 'Dost thou know what is happening?' 'What, then?' 'Thou art going to be boiled alive to-day. But hearken! when the King orders thee to jump into the boiling milk, beg him to allow me to be a witness of thy death. And hearken, furthermore,' the little horse went on, 'when I, being near thee, neigh for the first time, do not jump out of the bath. Nor must thou jump when I neigh the second time. But when I neigh the third time, then jump out of the bath and thou wilt emerge rejuvenated and far more handsome. Then the King, who is old, seeing how young and handsome thou hast become, will grow jealous, and will jump into the bath himself and be boiled, and thou shalt become espoused to the princess thyself.'

Well, the King orders him to jump into the boiling milk. 'I beg your Majesty and her Highness, to grant that my little horse be allowed to witness my death.' 'All right, we grant thy request.' The princess and the King look on. (But the princess knew that it was not this man, but the King himself who would be boiled alive.) The little horse arrived and watched the fool jump into the milk. He neighed once, he neighed twice, he neighed three times and the fool jumped out of the bath. The King looked at him: he had become rejuvenated and far more handsome. The King himself disrobed, and jumped into the milk—and was boiled alive.

Then the princess put her arms around the fool's neck and they embraced, and went to their marriage bed. The same day that the King was boiled alive, the ten eggs were transformed into the ten sisters of the princess, and the golden charger into her brother. The fool's six brothers married six of the sisters, and the other four remained as they were, and they lived happily by God's grace.

One day the fool mounted his little horse and went for a ride in the afternoon. He came into a wood and the little horse said to him: 'Dismount and cut off my head, and if thou wilt not cut off my head then I will cut off thine.' The fool began to weep, and in tears cut off the head of his little horse. Suddenly two little birds darted out of the horse and flew straight up into the sky. And the fool remained in his palace and lives there still by God's grace.

8. The Under-Gardener

There was a man who had three sons, two wise and one foolish. But this man was very poor. On what did he live? On fish.

One day he went fishing and caught eight. The two following days he caught three each day. But on the fourth day he caught thirteen. So he had plenty to eat.

On the fifth day he went fishing again but this time he only got a very pretty stone. When he returned home his wife asked him if he had caught anything, 'Only a pebble', he answered. Now it wasn't a pebble but a diamond. But he in his ignorance did not know what this stone was worth, so he put it on the stove. That night the stone shone brilliantly.

One day a King was passing that way. He said to his servant: 'Get down from the coach, and go and see what is glittering over there.' The servant entered the hut, and when he returned, the King asked him: 'Well, what *is* shining over there?' The man replied: 'Some sort of stone', for he too did not know its value.

The King alighted, himself, entered the hut and asked the fisherman if he would sell him the stone that sparkled so. The man, fool that he was, told the King he could have it for nothing. The King said: 'Think again.' Then the fisherman, after some thought, said: 'How much would you give me, Sire?' 'As much as thou wantest' was the answer. 'Oh! His Highness would never give me the sum I would ask of him.' 'Come, tell me', replied the King, 'and I will give thee as much as thou wantest.' 'Well then,' said the fisherman, 'give me a hundred florins.' 'I will give thee a thousand for it.' 'Please, your Majesty, do not make a mock of me and my stone', said the fisherman. 'But, thou fool of a man, I am not making fun of thee', replied the King. And he put his hand in his pocket, drew out a purse and paid him a thousand florins.

And now he is really wealthy, this fisherman. And he had a brother who also was rich when he himself was poor. So he said to his son, the foolish one: 'Go to my brother and borrow a bushel of wheat from him.' Well, the boy went. And his uncle asked him: 'What dost thou want?' 'I have come to ask you to lend us a bushel of wheat.' The rich man's only reply was that he would like to give him a thrashing. The fool returned to his father, who asked him: 'Well, what did he say to thee?' 'He wanted to thrash me.' 'Never mind, my son, one day he will come to me to ask me to lend him something.'

So this poor man bought two beautiful houses, three fields, and some fine oxen and cows and horses, in short he became a man of wealth. One day the man's brother came to pay him a visit, and said to him: 'Tell me, brother, how didst thou become so rich?' 'It was the good God who gave me my property: thou hast been rich up to the present, and now behold! I am even as rich as thou!' Then the rich brother asks him to lend him a hundred florins. The man replied: 'Once I sent my son to thee to ask thee to lend me a bushel of wheat, and thou wantedst to thrash him. So now I will lend thee nothing more.' So this brother had to take himself off because the other would not lend him anything. So he returned home.

Nevertheless this foolish son began to steal from his father and took what he stole to his uncle. And one day his father noticed that he had stolen something, so when he returned to the house his father asked: 'What didst thou take to my brother?' 'Nothing at all', replied the fool. The father took his stick and thrashed the lad till be bled, and then chased him out of the house.

Well, this fool came to a forest, where he began to weep because he was hungry. He lay down and fell asleep. A fairy came to him and said: 'Why dost thou weep, my boy?' 'Because my father thrashed me till I bled, and turned me out of his house.' 'Hush! do not weep; I will give thee a ring with which thou wilt only have to strike this rock three times. But be sure to remember exactly what I tell thee.'

The fairy disappeared, and the fool said to himself: 'Why

44

did she tell me to strike this rock thrice?' He struck three times, and out of the rock sprang a fine gentleman, who said to him: 'What dost thou desire, my lord?' 'I desire that a great feast be set before me.' Well, he ate and was satisfied, and he set forth, but before he left the forest he put a mark on this rock.

He was on his way, when a lord passed him. Now the boy was on foot, and this lord, noticing how handsome he was, said to him: 'Where goest thou, my lad?' 'I am trying to find a job somewhere.' 'Wilt thou enter my service?' asks this lord. 'With great pleasure, my lord.' This lord took him in his carriage and, when they reached his mansion, summoned his gardener: 'Look here, I have brought thee an assistant; take care not to do him any harm.' 'Very well, my lord.'

He led the boy into the garden. This lord gave him a becoming cap, a good pair of trousers, some good boots and a good shirt. He then had all the appearance of a very handsome young man.

Well, he had now been three weeks working under this gardener. And, one Sunday, the gardener gave him some bouquets to take to the lord's daughters. That was good! Having received the bouquets from the gardener he went off to an apple-tree and beneath it made two bouquets of copper for the two eldest daughters, and a bouquet of silver for the youngest. Well, he presented these bouquets to each of them. He returned to the gardener, who asked him: 'Hast thou delivered those bouquets to the young ladies?' 'I have delivered them.'

Then that morning the gardener went to church and the fool ran off. He went to the forest, he struck the rock three times with the ring, and a fine gentleman sprang out of the rock and stood before him. 'What does my lord desire?' 'I desire a suit of silver and a horse of silver.' Well, the silver suit and the silver horse were brought to him. The boy reached the church and he gave this same gardener a franc to look after his horse. In the church he seated himself beside the youngest lady. She asked him: 'Whence has my lord come?' 'From not very far away.' He gave her his golden ring and she gave him hers with her name engraved on it.

Immediately he quitted the church, mounted his horse,

and soon reached the forest, where he struck the rock thrice. The fine gentleman sprang out. 'What dost thou desire, my lord?' 'I desire that my horse should be hidden.'

He put on his ordinary clothes, did this boy, and returned to the house and the garden. The gardener said to him: 'Oh! if thou couldst but have seen what a grand prince was at church to-day! He gave me a franc for looking after his horse.' The boy begged him to take him to church with him the next Sunday. 'Most willingly will I do so.'

The lord's daughters say to their father: 'Oh, we saw such a handsome prince, his raiment was of silver and he had a silver horse.' The lord asked his daughters: 'Did you have any talk with him?' The eldest daughter answered: 'I did not speak to him.' But the youngest stood up and said: 'Father, if you will not whip me, I will confess everything.' 'I will not whip thee, my daughter, so just confess.' 'This prince gave me his ring, and I too gave him mine.' 'That is all right, my girl, we will easily find him.'

The next Sunday the gardener, as before, gave the boy three bouquets to deliver. And again he took them, went off to the apple-tree, and beneath it made two bouquets of silver for the two eldest daughters, and for his own (the youngest) girl a bouquet of gold. Well, he took these bouquets to the lord's mansion. The three young ladies appeared, and to the two eldest he gave bouquets of silver, but to his own girl a bouquet of gold. This youngest daughter who had received the golden bouquet presented him with a franc. He returned to the gardener, who asked him: 'Hast thou delivered the bouquets?' 'I have delivered them.' 'Good!'

Then once more he ran off to the forest, struck the rock three times with his ring, and a fine gentleman sprang out. 'What does my lord desire?' 'I desire a suit of gold and a horse of gold.' Well, the horse was brought to him, and the boy mounted it and reached the church. He handed his horse to the gardener to take care of and rewarded him with a ducat. He entered the church and seated himself beside his young lady. Everyone in the church and all the lords were lost in wonder at this prince arrayed in such splendid clothes. The youngest daughter gave him her handkerchief on which was embroidered her own and her father's names. The boy, in his

46

turn, gave her his handkerchief which also bore his name. He kissed the young lady and quitted the church.

He reached the forest, struck the rock three times with his ring, and a fine gentleman sprang out. 'What does my lord desire?' 'I desire that my horse and my raiment be hidden.' They were taken from him and hidden away.

He put on his ordinary clothes again and returned to the garden. The gardener asked him: 'Didst thou go to church?' 'No, I wasn't there.' 'Oh! if thou couldst but have seen the prince who was there! He had a suit of gold and a horse of gold. And it was I who looked after his horse, and he gave me a ducat.' 'Well and good!'

Then this lord said to his three daughters: 'Well, my daughters, what did you see in church?' 'Oh! father, we saw such a sight.' 'What then did you see?' 'We saw a prince in a suit of gold, and his horse also was of gold.' 'Did you talk to him?' 'We did not speak to him at all', answered the two eldest girls. But the youngest said: 'Yes, I spoke to him.' 'What didst thou say to him?' 'I invited him to come to dinner with us, and he replied he could not come until the third Sunday.'

Well, these three young ladies went out for a stroll in the garden, and sat down in an arbour and began to talk about the prince. The boy heard them and laughed aloud. Then they came out and asked him at what he was laughing. 'I am laughing at my own name.' Well, these ladies went away, and he was left by himself.

On the third Sunday the gardener told the boy he was going to church. The boy replied: 'Very good, sir, I will go there too.' 'But don't go and sit where the prince does.' Said the boy: 'I will sit in the belfry.' Well, he told the youth to take the bouquets to the young ladies. He took them, went off to the apple-tree and beneath it he made two bouquets of gold for the two eldest daughters, and for his own (the youngest) girl a bouquet of diamonds. He returned to the mansion, and gave the golden bouquets to the two eldest daughters, and the diamond bouquet to his own, the youngest, girl. She presented him with a crown for it, and he thanked her prettily and returned to the garden. The gardener asked him: 'Didst thou deliver the bouquets?' 'Yes, sir, I did.' 'Good!'

The gardener set out for church, and the boy ran off to the forest. He struck the rock thrice with his ring, and a fine gentleman sprang out. 'What does my lord desire?' 'I desire a suit of diamonds and a horse of diamonds.' Well, the horse was brought to him and the boy mounted and set off for the church. He gave his horse to the gardener to look after and rewarded him with a handful of silver. He entered the church, and his raiment shone with a brilliant light. He sat down beside the youngest daughter. She asked him: 'Is your Highness coming to dinner with us?' And he answered: 'Yes, I will come.'

They all four left the church together, he on horseback and they in a carriage. They reached the lord's mansion, and the lord was gratified. They served him with food and drink, and they intoxicated him, but he kept control of his senses. 'I beg you to excuse me, my lord and ladies,' he said, 'but I have far to travel; I will return to-morrow and then we can converse freely together.' All three young ladies escorted him to the door, but he was very intoxicated. 'Well,' said he, 'remain with God.' 'And do thou go with God', they replied. 'I will not return until to-morrow.'

Well, the young ladies went back to their house and he returned to the forest. He struck the rock with his ring thrice, and a fine gentleman appeared before him. 'What does my lord desire?' 'I desire you to hide my horse and my raiment.'

He dressed himself in his ordinary clothes and returned to the mansion, but deadly drunk. The gardener asked him: 'Where didst thou get so intoxicated?' 'What business is that of thine?' replied the boy. He put his ring on his finger and covered his face with the handkerchief that the youngest daughter had given him, and lay down in the arbour to have a sleep.

And who comes to the spot? This lord with the three daughters happens to be strolling in the garden, and the gardener complains to him that the boy is drunk and he would like to give him a thrashing. The lord enquires where he is sleeping. 'In the arbour'. The lord makes his way there with his three daughters, looks at the youth and recognizes on the boy's finger his daughter's ring with the name engraved on it. He calls the youngest girl and asks her: 'Is that

thy ring, my girl?' She looks at it. 'Yes, father, it is mine.'
'Oh! then this is the young man who was so cunning.' He
examines the kerchief and finds his own and his daughter's
names on it.

Well, they arouse the youth, but he is unable to lift up his
head. The lord called the gardener: 'Take this boy, and carry
him to my room.' The youngest girl says to the gardener:
'Was it thou who took care of this prince's horse?' 'Yes, my
lady, it was I.' 'Didst thou not recognize him?' 'No, my lady.'
It was not until he had carried him into the room that he
perceived that it was the same youth, and he was dumbfounded.

Well, the next morning the boy arose. 'Is it thou, then,
who hast been so cunning?' enquired the lord. 'I know nothing, my lord. How did you recognize that I was the man?'
The lord pointed to the ring that was still on his finger and
to the handkerchief: both handkerchief and ring belonged
to the youngest daughter. 'Well, which of my daughters dost
thou wish to take in marriage?' the lord asked him. 'Choose
her.' The boy said: 'I will take this, the youngest one.' And
so he married her. The lord gave him his whole fortune. And
they both lived with God.

9. The Lucky Simpleton

There was a poor country bumpkin who had no children
and lived all alone with his wife. He went to his brother's
house and borrowed a bushel of wheat and ground it. Fool
that he was, he put the flour outside beneath the window, and
the wind was so strong that it blew all his flour away. He began to weep, and his wife scolded him soundly for not bringing the flour into the house. 'Well, my little wife, since thou
scoldest me so bitterly I will go in search of the man who stole
my flour from me.' 'Yes, be off with thee!'

Then he went far into the world and came to a forest. He
saw a man perched up on a tree, and this creature asked the
poor fellow where he was going. 'I am going in search of the
thief who stole my flour.' 'And what was the name of this

49

thief?' enquired the man. 'He is called "The Wind"', answered the poor foolish one. 'Why! I am called the Wind myself', answered the man. Then the countryman gave him a box on the ears. The Wind said to him: 'Stop! don't hit me, but come along with me.' He went along with him and the man gave him a small table-cloth. 'When thou sayest, "Little table-cloth unfold thyself"', thou wilt instantly have food and drink.'

The poor fellow took this table-cloth and went far into the fields, and said to his cloth, 'Unfold thyself!' And behold! There was spread before him food and drink.

Further on he had to pass by a tavern kept by a Jew. This man, on catching sight of him, invited him in. He gave him some brandy, intoxicated him and then made him go to bed. Now, towards nightfall this simpleton blurted out to the Jew: 'Be sure not to tell my table-cloth to unfold.' 'Be not afraid, for surely thou knowest me better than that', replied the Jew. This simpleton fell asleep. The landlord took the table-cloth from him, retired into a small room and said aloud: 'Little table-cloth, unfold thyself.' And immediately there was spread before him meat and drink. Then what did this Jew do? He gave the simpleton another cloth and took this one and hid it.

The next morning the countryman arose, ordered some brandy for himself and set off on his journey, with God's grace. The poor fellow came back to his wife and said: 'See, wife, now we have got a treasure.' His wife, overjoyed, made him show it to her. He showed her the table-cloth and bade her order it to unfold. She asked: 'What for?' 'So that thou wilt immediately have before thee food and drink.' Said his wife: 'Do thou give the order thyself, since thou knowest the way, and since thou hast found the thief.' Then the simpleton cried: 'Little table-cloth, unfold thyself.' There was nothing to eat or drink! He seized the table-cloth and tore it to pieces.

Then (in a rage) he went forth to look for the Wind again. He came to the Wind's home did this poor simpleton, and asked him: 'What sort of a table-cloth didst thou give me?' 'I gave thee a good one.' 'What! thou didst give me a cloth from which I only satisfied my appetite twice, and which on the third occasion gave me nothing at all.'

Then the Wind said: 'Listen! I will give thee a loaf of bread which even if thou cuttest a slice from it will again become whole.' Well, the simpleton went far into the fields, cut a slice of bread from his loaf, and behold! the loaf became whole again.

He reached the same Jew's tavern. The landlord seeing him on the road, called out to him and enquired how he was. 'Quite well', replied the simpleton. The Jew invited him in and gave him a glass of brandy free of charge. The simpleton ordered himself another glass, and became intoxicated. Towards evening he blurted out to the Jew: 'Be sure not to cut a slice of bread from my loaf.' Nevertheless the Jew did cut a slice and he saw that the loaf became whole again. Then the Jew took this loaf and put another in its place near the man's pillow.

In the morning the poor simpleton arose and had another glass of brandy brought to him, but he never paid for it. He took his loaf under his arm and returned to his wife's home and said to her: 'Cut a slice of bread for thyself, wife.' His wife was very pleased because she was hungry, so she cut off half the loaf. The simpleton was watching her: his loaf did not become whole again. He tasted a morsel and murmured: 'Whatever sort of bread has that fellow given me?'

He went back to the Wind. When the Wind saw him approaching in the forest, he called out: 'Why hast thou returned?' 'I have come back, because thou art deceiving me; if thou meanest to give me a present, pray give me something good.'

'Then, listen!' said the Wind; 'take this lamb and when thou sayest to it, "Shake thyself", it will drop ducats for thee!' The simpleton went far into the fields and said to his lamb: 'Shake thyself', and, lo and behold! ducats and francs poured out from its body. So he called out: 'Stop, my lamb.'

He was passing by that same tavern, when the Jew saw him and called him in. He entered. And now this simpleton who used to be poor had plenty of money. The Jew gave him something to drink and made him tipsy. Towards nightfall the simpleton blurted out: 'Be sure not to say to my lamb, "Shake thyself"'. The Jew said reassuringly: 'Be not afraid, for surely thou knowest me better than that.' The simpleton fell asleep. The Jew took the lamb into a small room and said aloud: 'Lamb, shake thyself.' But the Jew did not know what to say to make it stop, until his little son called out: 'Whoa! lamb', and the lamb stopped. When it had finished, the Jew said: 'Where on earth shall I go to find another lamb to put back in place of this one?' So he went to the castle and bought a lamb and brought it back for the poor fellow.

In the morning, the simpleton arose, treated himself to a glass of brandy and set forth and went home to his wife. He gave her the money and cried: 'See, wife, what I am going to do with this lamb.' 'Well, what art thou going to do?' He cried to the lamb: 'Shake thyself.' The lamb would not stir. Then the simpleton seized it and slaughtered the animal. 'Take this and eat it, by God's grace', he said to his wife, and as for me I will go once again and search for the thief.

He went back to the Wind, who asked him why he had come. 'For the love of God, why dost thou treat me as if I were a fool?' said the poor country bumpkin. 'Oh, well! come with me.' Then the Wind cut him two great cudgels and said: 'If thou art in distress thou must say to these cudgels: "Strike!" and afterwards, "Be hidden". But', added the Wind, 'say naught to them until thou hast reached the Jew's tavern.'

Well, this poor simpleton walks on, and the Jew catching sight of him calls out to him. He enters the inn, orders some brandy, and drinks from morning till night. At last after nightfall when he was preparing to go to sleep, he said to the Jew: 'Beware of saying to my cudgels: "Strike!" ' 'Be not afraid, thou knowest me too well for that.' The simpleton fell asleep, the Jew seized both his clubs, summoned his wife and his two sons, and shut himself up in his room with them. Then he cried out: 'Cudgels, strike!' Then these cudgels gave the Jew and his wife a sound drubbing and killed the two little boys.

The countryman heard this terrible uproar, jumped out of bed and saw that his cudgels were no longer there. He opens his door in a rage and the Jew and his wife scream out to him: 'We will restore all we have taken from thee.' So he calls to the cudgels: 'Be hidden.' The cudgels disappeared. Then the Jew restored to the simpleton first his tablecloth, then his loaf of bread and finally his lamb.

The man returned to his wife's house. He took the two cudgels, smashed them and burned them—fool that he was! Then he presented the little table-cloth to his wife and said: 'Unfold thyself.' And there was spread before them food and drink. Then he cut off half the loaf and his wife beheld that the loaf became whole again. And she rejoiced. Finally he cried to the lamb: 'Shake thyself', and it dropped francs and ducats. He ordered a fine palace to be built for him, and there he lives with his wife, by the grace of God.

RUSSIAN

Recorded by V. N. Dobrowolski

—————————◄═══►⸂—————————

10. The Devil who Courted a Gypsy Girl

Once upon a time there was a girl. The girl and her mother lived alone with her father, so there were only the three of them; they lived in great comfort. The girl went out to wash shirts, and she beholds a Gypsy man riding on horseback, handsome, so handsome that there was no other like him. He says: 'Hail to you, girl! where do you live?' And she says: 'Over there not far away. But where do you?' 'You go ahead! I will follow directly.' And he came to their tent and tied up his horse, and he entered that tent, and says: 'Hail to you, old man!' The old man asks him: 'What sort of a man are you?' He says: 'I am a Gypsy, and I am on my travels— you don't happen to know of anyone willing to barter?' The old man says: 'Over there not far away, lives a gentleman; only he doesn't like Gypsies.' But the man says: 'All right! it doesn't matter!'

They set out, just the two of them. They went on and on. The old Gypsy stopped behind at a distance, but yon fellow went into the mansion. The gentleman asks: 'Who is that fellow who has just come in?' The footman says: 'A Gypsy.' 'Send him in here to me.' He went into the room. The gentleman received him, and asked: 'Did you come by yourself?' So he says to the gentleman: 'No, I have a companion waiting for me yonder in the field.' The gentleman sent the footman after him, saying: 'Go, give him a call.' And the old man thought that they were pursuing him, and he began to run far away—with difficulty they called him back. Then he entered the mansion. And the Gypsy fellow says: 'Have you nothing to barter, sir?' And the gentleman says: 'Yes'. And they brought out to him from the stall a better horse than his own, and they made an exchange. Also the gentleman gave him in addition money, much money he gave him.

The pair came back to the tent, and the fellow says: 'Old man, would you consent to give your daughter to me, a Gypsy?' And the old man answers: 'Just as it suits my daughter.' Then the girl says: 'I will go with him.' But he replies: 'I will come with my father to a betrothal with you in the course of a week.' So he comes with his father and made a match with that girl. And he says: 'I wish you would give me your daughter without the wedding ceremony; I have no time just now to celebrate the wedding. I am stopping on the border of a gentleman's estate, and our horses have trampled his corn; so I have no time now; I must be off to that gentleman and pay for the corn. Well, are you agreed? Will you give your daughter to me, the young Gypsy? But after the enquiry is over, then we will celebrate the wedding.' The old man says: 'Ask the girl if she consents. If she consents then I am agreeable.' And they asked the girl. And the girl said: 'If I don't go with this man, then I will not go with any man, and I shall be weeping because of you all my days.' So the old fellow gave his consent.

They put the horses to and off they went; they drove maybe fifty versts, and they pitched their tents. And the girl took the pail and went for some water, and the children, the little ones, ran after her. And she noticed little horns on the heads of those children. And she began to weep because these little naked things were not human at all, but devils. And she began to beseech her own Gypsy: 'Oh, do let us go to my father on a visit!' But he did not want to go. But she persuaded him, and he agreed to accompany her. And they put to and went back to her father.

Her father and mother were glad that the girl had come to them on a visit. The old man mounted his horse and went to fetch brandy. And he sat down to drink the brandy with his son-in-law. And the son-in-law got drunk and lay down under the canopy bed. And in tears she cries to her father: 'Alas! do you go as quick as you can for the parson, make the parson come.' And the parson comes, and the people crowded in. And he began to bless the tent. And that fellow noticed it, as he lay there under the bed, and he smashed the bed and the tent—and he fled away. But the girl only survived him for one week and then she died.

LATVIAN

Recorded by Professor Paul Ariste

———————————✦———————————

11. The Wind-Maiden

Once upon a time there was a rich Gypsy. He had a young son of eighteen years, who carved beautiful violins. They dwelled in a lovely forest. One morning he suddenly caught sight of a beauteous maiden in the trees, whom folk called Rusalka of the Woods, or the Wind-Maiden.

The young Gypsy was carving a beautiful violin, and suddenly towards dawn he looked up: again the maiden appeared. The youth said to her: 'Come down! if thou dost not, I will hang myself.' The maiden hardly knew how to talk to him. She says: 'I am naked.' Said the youth: 'I will go and fetch my mother's clothes.' He went off and stole his mother's clothes.

Rusalka whispered to him: 'Move further away.' The youth went behind his van and watched her. She was so beautiful that he could not wait until she had dressed herself. He seized her, and took her and put her in his van. His parents raised a great outcry when they woke up.

They fled to the town and dwelled there for a year. A child was born to them. The nymph's nails were so long that she could not wear shoes on her feet. The youth bathed them in hot water until the nails softened and then he cut them. He combs her hair, while she sat on a bench at his feet. Being blind, she does not know how to tend her hair. She speaks to him thus: 'If I suffer the Town Wind I cannot suffer the Forest Wind, or my menfolk would scold me.'

But the Gypsy youth forgot all about this. One Friday he says to his father: 'Come to the forest.' They went to the forest. The youth begins carving a violin in his van. His parents went into the town to buy something, and their son also set forth to barter. His wife remained at home.

Suddenly the wind arose. The girl pulled off her clothes and left herself naked. All at once she began to weep and said to the Wind: 'It is not for me to follow thee. Do thou go and break thy neck! As for me I must now follow after my little boy.'

Presently the youth comes home and looks around him: there is no wife. He began to weep. And soon after his parents return. Their son wants to shoot himself. His parents have a talk together and say to him: 'Let us leave the forest.' Says their son: 'I will not budge.'

Suddenly the youth looks about him, and in the morning sees his little boy seeking for food. And all at once the youth understood. He nosed about, and suddenly sees that his wife has come back, and he rushes after her behind the van. She presently fetches some water, heats it and bathes the child. Her husband gave a bound and seized her by the hair.

He shouted out to his parents: 'Get up at once, I have caught my wife.' His parents rose, put in the horses and drove back to the town. They lived in the town for twenty-eight years until their hair grew grey. And so she Rusalka, the Wood-nymph, forgot the forest for the sake of her fine son: she forgot the forest, Rusalka utterly forgot the forest.

12. The Dead Lover

There was once a poor man and he is a widower. He has many sons and one lovely daughter ten years old. She used to go the round of the houses with a begging-bag on her shoulders and a pail in her hand, hoping to get something.

In the forest was a rich man who was a prince. He had a handsome son who used to travel on horseback. This youth looked about him, and saw a lovely girl coming his way. He waited for the girl and begged a drink of milk from her. She was so beautiful that the boy's strength failed him. 'Where dost thou live?' he asked. She told him where she lived, in a cutting beyond the forest. He told her that he generally went out in the mornings; at ten o'clock he would start.

The girl looked out for him. The youth appeared, and had

a talk with her. Said he: 'In the morning my mother will come and say to thee: "Sew this skirt of mine." Thou must mend it, so that no one could find any brack in it.'

The youth gave the girl needles and thread. His mother came and said to the girl: 'Mend my skirt, the horse tore it.' Now his mother was a witch. The girl replied: 'I will mend it.' And she mended it so neatly that no one could find a brack in it.

The mother went home and said to her son: 'Thou shalt not take that girl to wife, even if thou art broken-hearted.' The youth died, and they buried him. But the girl did not know. At night the youth appears and said to the girl: 'Come away with me.' The girl replied: 'How can I go? I have young brothers, they will be afraid if I leave them.' Said the youth: 'Heed not, no one will touch them.'

The girl arrayed herself. She put on fifteen petticoats. She mounted his horse. Quoth the youth: 'The Dead carries the living.' 'Do not frighten me', said the girl. 'Heed not, foolish maiden, I said it with a purpose.' He took her to the church-yard and he says to the girl: 'Do thou make the bed!' 'I do not know how to in a coffin', she answered. 'I cannot: do thou make the bed.' The youth made the bed and then said: 'Take off thy clothes.' The girl took off her skirt. She took off all her petticoats, until she was left in her smock. At one o'clock the cock crew. At one o'clock the youth fell back into his coffin.

The girl fled to the priest and cried: 'Hear my plaint.' He answered: 'What hast thou to say?' She replied that her bridegroom had taken her to the churchyard (she did not know that the youth was dead) and had said to her: 'The Dead carries the living.' 'I answered: "Do not frighten me." He took me to the churchyard and bade me make the bed in the coffin. I said: "I know not how to make the bed." Then the youth went into the coffin and made the bed. It was one o'clock and the cock crew.'

Then at five o'clock the priest came to the spot and saw the youth lying in his coffin. He took the coffin into the church. Then the priest collected a number of maidens and had them all dressed in the same garments so that the youth could not distinguish one from the other.

58

At ten o'clock the priest sees the foot of the corpse move, and at eleven o'clock the youth rose from his coffin to seek his maiden. Then the priest saw that he means to take this girl. The youth walked past all the other maidens, and seized hold of her.

The priest picked up a Bible and straightway the youth fell back into his coffin. The priest set to and cut his throat—and lo! blood flowed from it as from a living man!

13. The Princess and the Farm-Boy

Once upon a time there was a poor old man who went to a farmer and said: 'Take my boy to work in the fields. And what wilt thou give him for the summer?' 'I will give him three good loaves and three roubles.'

So the boy went to work in the fields, and as he was coming home he meets an old beggar who says to him: 'My lad, couldst thou possibly give me a good loaf and one rouble?' 'Indeed, I can', says the boy.

He went on further and met another old man. 'Couldst thou give me a good loaf and a rouble?' He did. And that old man gave him a whistle, and told him to go home.

He went home and he begins to whistle, and he sees that there are twelve little golden pigs in the stye. And as he whistles those piglets begin to dance. His father sees this and is so overcome with merriment that he cannot speak.

The boy sets off and comes to the King's window. He begins to whistle and those little pigs dance a hundred dances. A young princess appears and says to him: 'Sell me a little pig.' 'I will not sell to thee for money.' 'What dost thou desire?' 'I desire to see thee display thyself up to thy knees.' Now up to her knees she is golden. The boy gave her that little pig.

She carried home the piglet, but it would not dance. She came again to the boy and says: 'Why won't he dance?' 'Because he is alone, and is used to having the rest of the litter near him.' 'Well, sell me another one beside him.' 'Dost thou not know that I will not sell for money?' 'What then dost thou desire?' 'I desire thee to strip thyself naked.' 'Well', thought she to herself, 'how much this boy knows!' She stripped herself naked. She had the mark of a golden raspberry on her breast and she had golden hairs.

The King prepared to hold a ball to which everyone must come. 'The man who declares what mark the princess has on her body', he proclaims, 'shall take her as wife.' So they all came to make their answer. The farm-boy went also. Now they all had their say, but not one of them answered rightly.

A priest declared: 'She has golden hairs.' The King replies: 'What else has she?' 'I know nothing more.'

The boy enquires: 'Am I also allowed to have my say?' 'Yes, you are allowed.' 'Well', said the boy outright: 'As far as her knees she is golden, on her breast is a golden raspberry and golden hairs, and lower down three diamond hairs.' 'The truth!' declared the King. 'Well, now thou shalt take her for thyself.'

Then said the priest: 'See, the point is that it was I who said she had golden hairs, and he only spoke after me.' So the King declared: 'To-night I will put you all three in one room to sleep, and the one to whom she turns her face he shall take her for himself.' 'All right!'

The boy went into the town, he bought chocolate, wine, oranges, a hundred dainties.

Now evening fell. They have to go into that chamber. The princess went in to lie down. The boy sat with the priest at a bench to play cards. They drink wine. The boy put into the bottle a strong drench. Well! now they enter the room to lie down. The boy says 'I am not going to lie down, I have a pain.' The priest says: 'So have I.' Says the boy: 'Let us relieve ourselves.' 'Yes, let us', replies the priest. They do. . . . The priest eats his own excrement. The boy eats chocolate. Now they return to rest. Says the boy: 'Do thou lie in front, I will lie behind her.' 'All right, let us repose.'

The princess arises, smells an unpleasant smell. Quoth she: 'My heart sayeth, this is a mere man, and he stinks too, does this man!' And the priest is lying down, and the princess wonders if the boy is all right, for she is not sure that it is the priest who smells. She turned to the boy's side.

In the morning the King comes in. He sees the princess is

lying facing the boy, and that the priest is behind her. The King ordered them to robe the boy in royal apparel. And the priest they cast into the stables.

And so I ate and drank and came to you to tell you this tale. And who gave that whistle to the farm-boy? God!

BULGARIAN

Recorded by B. Gilliat-Smith

14. The Tale of a God

There is an old man and he has a daughter. And the daughter is small, she cannot yet wash her head, she is eaten up with lice. The daughter says: 'O father, why do you not take a wife that she may wash us, for we are eaten up with lice?'

The father took a wife, and that wife had a daughter of her own. There happened what happened, and the wife says to her stepdaughter: 'Hear me, O harlot, take this white wool, go to the river, and stop there until you have washed it, and made it become black; if you return home before you have turned it into black wool, I will kill you.'

The girl got ready, made a cake out of dung, and went off to the river. She started washing the wool; one evening, two evenings, three evenings she is seated there. The more she washes the wool, the whiter it becomes, but it will never become black. Behold a god descends, and asks the girl: 'What are you doing, child?' 'Behold, father, I am washing wool.' 'Eh, why are you washing it?' 'Behold I have a stepmother, who has sent me to wash this wool; until I turn it from white into black, I am not to go home, otherwise she said she will kill me.' Thus she spoke to the father. The god went off. What does he see in the fire? A cake of dung buried in the ashes. The god strikes it with his stick, makes a new cake, and behold it rises. He goes up to the girl. 'Ha, my child, go and take out your cake and eat it.' 'But, father, it is not yet baked.' 'Ha! go, my child', says the god, 'it is baked.' When the girl goes to the spot, what does she see? A fresh cake, well leavened. She sits down to eat, and eats the whole of the cake, every crumb of it.

The god comes up to her: 'Child, louse me.' The god bent

down in the arms of the girl; the girl louses him. The girl makes a dart at an insect. The god says: 'What are you hitting at?' The girl says: 'Silver, father.' The god says: 'Child, wait till I turn round, that you may search me from this side too.' The god turned round to the other side. The girl strikes again. The god asks: 'What are you hitting at, child?' 'Behold, Father, gold!' The god said: 'Well my child, wherever you walk may you be clothed in silver and gold, and burn and shine like a candle!' The girl began to burn and shine, clad in silver and in gold. The god departs. He gives one blow with his stick at the wool, and turns it from white into black. 'Now, my child, take your wool and be-gone.' What does the girl see? The god has made the wool black. The girl picks up the wool, and went off home.

The stepmother sees the girl shining and burning with beauty clad in silver and gold. The stepmother arises from her chair, and places the girl in it that she may be seated. To her own daughter she says: 'See, child, may you eat her vitals and her excrement! Look here! you I always feed with butter and eggs, but for her I make bread from dung to nourish her. Quickly, then, harlot, do you also begone.' The mother gives her white wool, and prepares for her butter and eggs; her daughter set forth, and she too went to the river.

She went to the same spot, and does her washing in the river: one evening, two evenings, three evenings. Behold yonder comes the god: 'Good evening, child.' The girl calls out to the god: 'What an old ass to ask me what I am doing!' Again the god says: 'Good evening.' Again the girl answers: 'What an old ass to ask me what I am doing!' The god says to her: 'Ah, child, may the god now make you half a she-ass, and half a woman, and may all the he-asses there are follow you, so that you will not be able to raise your head by reason of these jack-asses.' The girl set off for home. What does her mother see? Half a she-ass, and half a human being, and all the he-asses following her. The mother starts driving the asses away, and brings the girl indoors.

The mother makes her daughter a frock exactly like the other girl's, so that she too burns and shines with silver and gold.

* * *

The King's son heard about this and fell ill. Oh! alas! he
is about to die. The King asks him: 'My son, what ails you?
Have you not got food to eat, have you not got money?' 'I
do not want your money, nor your food. But I want . . . there
is an old woman's daughter, it is her I want, let them bring
her to me.'

The woman hears that the King's son means to come and
take the girl, her stepdaughter. She arises and arrays her own
daughter, so that she burns and shines with silver and gold.
She takes her stepdaughter, places her under the trough, and
hides her. The carriages arrive. She brings out her daughter
and bundles her into the carriage.

There is a cock and he crows: 'Kikirigoo, the pretty one is
under the trough and the she-ass in the carriage.' Again the
cock crows: 'Kikirigoo, the pretty one is under the trough
and the she-ass in the carriage.' Now the King had an old
witch and she says to him: 'O King, hear, how the cock is
crowing.' The King listens intently. Again the cock crows:
'Kikirigoo, the pretty one is under the trough, and the she-
ass is in the carriage.' The King hears. When he starts lifting
the trough, what does he see? The stepdaughter, and she is
burning and shining. When she cries she pours forth pearls,
when she laughs she pours forth roses. The King seizes her,
and throws her into the carriage. They started to go to his
palace.

They drove on and on. Then the stepmother starts making
a dishful of Turkish delight, all salted, and gave some to her
stepdaughter, and she ate. And when she had eaten, she was
dying for water, for she had eaten salted lukum. 'Come,
Mother, give me a little water, that I may drink.' The stepmother says: 'Well, child, come here that I may pluck out one
of your eyes, and then I will give you something to drink.'
The girl says: 'Well Mother, since you mean to pick a quarrel
with me, pluck out one of my eyes, if you so desire.' Again
the girl begs: 'Come, Mother, give me a little water, I am
dying for water. It was you who gave me the salted lukum,
and now you won't give me water to drink.' The stepmother
says again: 'Come here, that I may pluck out your eye, and
then I will give you something to drink.' The girl saw what
she saw. She gave her eye, the stepmother plucked it out. She

gave her water, just one drop to drink. Says the girl: 'Come, Mother, you have plucked out my eye, at least give me enough water to drink that I may satisfy my thirst.' The stepmother answers: 'Come here, that I may pluck out the other eye too, and I will give you enough to drink.' The girl says: 'Well, Mother, how comes it that you are so enraged against me that you want to pluck out this eye too, so that I shall be for ever blind in both eyes?' 'Eh, child, it is just as you please. . . .' The girl saw what she saw. She gave the other eye too, the stepmother plucked it out. Then she gave her the goblet, and the girl drank her fill.

They drove on and on as far as some thorn bushes. The stepmother pushes the girl out of the carriage, and casts her among the thorns. They went on, right to the King's palace. One day, two days pass at the King's, they eat, they drink.

*　　*　　*

Now there was a Turk, and he had twenty sons. All day they are dying of hunger, and they continually go shooting birds and sparrows to eat instead of bread.

Day broke. The old Turk bestirred himself. He was on his way, going hunting, when what does he see? In the thorn bushes a girl who burns and shines with silver and gold. The Turk approached her. As he walks, he makes a shuffling noise with his feet. The girl hears as she is lying on her back. 'Who are you that are coming near to me? If you are a young man, be my brother; if you are an old man, be my father; if you are an old woman, be my mother; if you are a young girl, be my sister.' The Turk went up to her. 'I am an old Turk.' 'I pray you, take these pearls and these roses. The King is preparing a marriage feast; do you go thither, and sell them, crying: "I sell pearls, I sell roses." But should they ask you whether you will be paid in cash, explain that you do not require money, but say: "I took them for eyes, I give them for eyes." '

The stepmother came out: 'Heigh! old man, come here. What are you selling?' And the Turk cries: 'I sell pearls, I sell roses.' The stepmother, the girl's stepmother, calls to the Turk and asks: 'How much money do you want for the pearls?' The Turk says: 'I do not sell for money. I took them

65

for eyes, I give them for eyes.' The stepmother took the pearls. She takes an eye from her pocket and gives it to him. She asks: 'But what do you want for the roses?' 'Those also I took for eyes, and exchange them for eyes.' The daughter says to her mother: 'Mother give the other eye too, the harlot's eye, and buy me the roses as well.' She gives the other eye too, and buys her the roses. The Turk got both eyes. He departed and went back to the girl.

Three geese are flying overhead. The eldest goose said: 'Heigh! yonder girl is blind, and she is lying on her back: let her take heed and hearken, let her search around her. I will drop the feather near her, let her search and stretch out and feel all around her, and take that feather and go her way. And yonder is a well, let her go up to the well, and stoop thrice, and moisten the feather in the water of the well, it is holy water from the well of Zemzem. Thrice let her dip the feather into the water, and wash her eyes with the feather. And they will become twice as beautiful as those she had before.' The girl heard.

The Turk came. 'Have you returned?' asks the girl. 'Look around me and see if there is a feather near me.' The Turk searched and found it. The Turk says: 'Behold the feather near you.' He picked it up, gave it to the girl. 'Take hold of me', she says, 'and lead me. Behold, yonder is a well, leave me near it.' The Turk leads her up to the well. 'Now go', says the girl to the Turk, 'and stand over yonder.' She left him a half-hour's distance away from her, and then went up to the well. She stooped again, and once more moistened the feather, and drew it across her eyes; she stooped once more, and yet again moistened the feather, and drew it across her eyes—for the third time. Her eyes became twice as beautiful as those she had before. She called to the Turk: 'Come now, close up to me.' Then she took money and gave him two hats full, filled his hat up to the brim with levs and coins and napoleons as baksheesh, for his having brought her the eyes. And the Turk departed.

* * *

Then she set forth and went to the King's gate. She turns herself into a pear-tree, and the branches break with the

66

abundance of fruit. What does the King see when he arises in the morning? In front of the gate is a pear tree, bowed down by reason of the pears. When the stepmother sees it, she says to her daughter: 'Child, undoubtedly this is the harlot; she got back her eyes when I bought you the pearls and the roses. I gave up the eyes and she recovered.'

The daughter thereupon pretended to be ill. Her mother says: 'Child, I will roll cakes and place them under you in bed. As soon as evening falls, your husband will come. Then you must turn over on to the cakes. Krsh! krsh! krsh! they will crackle under you, and you must sigh. If your husband asks you why, you must say: "I have had a vision, that if you cut down that pear tree, and give me of the root to eat, I will recover."'

The King's son lays hold of, and cuts down, the pear tree. The stepdaughter understands, takes flight, and turns herself into a poplar tree in front of the King's gate. After cutting down the pear tree, he came to his wife. 'Has your illness passed from you?' he asks. The wife says with a sigh: 'No! it has not passed, I am very sick. I have had a vision, that if you cut down that poplar tree and I eat of it, I shall recover.' The King's son goes out, cuts down the poplar tree, and hacks it all to pieces. Now there is an old Gypsy woman sitting opposite. Says she: 'Why do I not go and take a piece of that poplar wood, to fasten on to my door, where it is broken?' The old Gypsy woman takes a piece of wood from the poplar tree and nails it to her door.

Evening fell. The stepdaughter went thither to question her. 'Bravo, old woman, because you took that wood you raised my heart, my life. Do not worry any longer, old woman', says the girl; 'as for me, whatever you want I will bring it to you—everything: your sugar, your coffee, straightway to your feet.'

One night, two nights pass, and the old woman keeps asking her: 'Eh, child, where does your heart really lie?' For she, the stepmother, bids the old woman enquire where the girl's heart and her strength lie. The girl says: 'Come, old woman, what advantage is it to you to ask where my heart and where my strength lie? I will tell you, but wait until I can have a coffin made for me opposite the King's palace.' The girl arises, and has a glass coffin made for her; and all around her, where she cried, she poured forth pearls, where she laughed she strewed roses.

Evening came. She comes to the old woman: 'Heigh, old woman, you want me to tell you where my heart and where my strength lie. Come with me as far as yonder point, and I will tell you.' They went as far as the coffin. The girl entered, and said: 'Behold I will tell you where my heart is, and immediately I shall die. You are the cause of it.' The girl said: 'My heart is that piece of wood; the moment you strike any part of it I shall die, and if anyone seize me by the foot by the little toe, immediately I shall expire.' The girl spoke, and fell dead.

Where she lies dead in her coffin she shines and burns with beauty: around her are nothing but pearls, around her nothing but roses; she is hidden in the pearls. Evening fell.

Day broke. The King's son passes by. What does he see? Before him a coffin, all of glass. Inside lies a girl, dead, but shining and burning. Where she cried she poured forth pearls, where she laughed she strewed roses. The King's son remained enamoured of the girl in the coffin, and he went and embraced her in that coffin. She became pregnant from the King's son. She bore a male child. The boy lies by her, playing with a silver apple in his hand. That boy beside his mother, when he cried, he poured forth pearls, when he laughed he strewed roses.

One day, two days, one week pass. The King's son, all alone, says to himself: 'God! Why do I not go to see that girl, out of love? It is a long time since I have been to her.' The King's son bestirs himself, draws near to her. What does he see? In her arms the male child she had borne, with a silver apple in his hand, and he is playing with the apple. When that boy cried he poured forth pearls, when he laughed he strewed roses. The King's son enters the coffin and takes the boy in his arms.

The little boys says: 'I will not go with you, I cannot leave my mother alone. Could I but go, I would violate the little mother of that old woman, for she destroyed my mother.' The King's son asks the boy: 'How did the old woman destroy your mother?' 'How indeed? You, if you love me and

68

my mother, do you go to the old woman. She has a door, do not go to the first one, but to the second. On the door is a piece of wood, cut from a poplar; do but bring it hence, and my mother will rise.'

He snatches the piece of wood from the door, and goes from there back to the girl. The girl says, 'Achoo! Surely I was asleep.' 'You slept indeed, for the old woman destroyed you.' The girl arose. The King's son embraced her. The girl sat down and told her story bit by bit to the youth.

'As for me, you must know that you sent your father for me to come and take me for your sake. Your father came with carriages to take me for your sake, for you had cast your desire upon me. Your father's coming destroyed me. I have a stepmother, and she has a daughter. Scarcely had she seen the carriages arriving than she threw me under the trough and bundled her own daughter into the carriage. We have a cock. The cock crows: "Kikirigoo, the pretty one is under the trough and the she-ass in the carriage." Again the cock crows: "Kikirigoo, the pretty one is under the trough and the she-ass in the carriage!" "Oh! King, hearken, hearken," cried an old witch, "how the cock is crowing." For the third time again the cock crows: "Kikirigoo, the pretty one is under the trough and the she-ass in the carriage." The King hears, takes me out from under the trough. What do the people see? Where I cried I poured forth pearls, where I laughed I strewed roses.

'My stepmother threw me also into the carriage. We drove on and on, and she made me lukum, a dishful of lukum, all salted, and I ate, and was dying for water. I begged water from her, and she said to me: "Come here, that I may pluck out one of your eyes, and I will give you water." I said to her: "Why! Mother, how enraged you must be against me, to pluck out my eye, in order to give me a little water!" I gave her one eye; she took out the eye, gave me one drop of water. I begged of her: "Come, Mother, give me at least enough to satisfy my thirst." "Well! come here, that I may pluck out the other eye too, and I'll give you as much water as you want to drink." I give her the other eye too, my stepmother plucks it out. We went as far as some thorn bushes. She gave me a push and I fell into the thorns. Then she hurries off with her own daughter to you. You eat, you drink, you prepare a marriage feast.

'She forced me to stop in the midst of the thicket, until from where I was lying, I could hear someone rustling. I asked him if he were a young man, to be my brother; if he were an old man, to be my father. Then a Turk came up to me. I told him you were celebrating a marriage feast; I cried, I poured forth pearls; I laughed, I poured forth roses. I sent him to cry aloud: "Pearls I sell, roses I sell." My stepmother came out. She bought pearls. She asked: "What do you want for them?" The Turk said: "For eyes I took them, for eyes I sell them." He got one of my eyes; and then she wanted roses, for them too he got my other eye.

'He brought me my eyes. Three geese were flying overhead. The eldest goose says: "Heigh! let that little maiden hearken to me, I will drop a feather near her, so that she can search round about her and find it. There is a well hard by, let her go and dip the feather in it and draw the feather across her eyes and she will recover her sight." The Turk drew near. I told him to search round about me for the feather. He found the feather which the three geese had dropped for me. He led me to the well. I dipped the feather in the well and drew it three times across my eyes: I recovered my sight. I gave that Turk a present and I came here.

'I turned myself into a pear tree. Your wife pretended to be ill, and made you have the tree cut down. I turned myself into a poplar tree, your wife made you have that cut down too. Then there was an old woman whom my stepmother set to enquire where lay my heart and strength. She took a piece of wood from the poplar and nailed it to her door. Says she: "Tell me, child, where is your heart?" I told her where my heart lay, and I fell down dead.'

He summons the old woman: 'Who gave you a mind to enquire where lay her heart?' The old woman says: 'O King, from you I cannot hide aught. You are King from that day to this day. You have a wife, and she has a mother. Ceaselessly, to-day, to-morrow, every day she urged me to ask the girl where lay her heart. And the girl said to me: "I will tell you where lies my heart, but I shall die." She told me: "My heart is in that piece of wood. Nail it fast to your door, and seize me by the little toe of my foot, and I shall fall down dead." And she fell down and she died.'

The youth went home, questions his wife: 'Come you, why are you ill?' 'I ail nothing, I have no pain.' 'Now you', he says to his mother-in-law, 'do you want forty horses or forty knives?' 'Let there be for us forty horses, let there be forty knives for our enemies, that they may perish all the sooner.' So he binds her to the tails of forty horses, and gives the horses a single lash, and they tear her to pieces. His wife also he ordered to be torn to pieces.

There is the Tale! Here is your Health!

15. The Merchant's Daughter

There was a merchant and he had a shop. Now no shop carried on business so successfully as his shop. His was a most important shop, and he had twenty servants and one daughter.

Midday came, all the servants shut up the shop, and went to eat bread. The daughter said to her father: 'O Father, it is not necessary for you to keep a shop. Go in front of the shop, and stand there, and take a bag of money: and as all the young assistants pass by give them their wages one by one, even unto the last of them, that they may leave for good.' The father says: 'Wait, Sinko, supposing I do pay them off, who will look after the shop afterwards?' The daughter said: 'I will look after it alone.' Said the father: 'Stay, Sinko, twenty assistants are unable to serve the customers. What will you do alone?' 'Be not worried, father, fret not! I will both attend to the till and serve the customers.'

Now the girl went, and she opened the shop. She put all the wares in order, and she seats herself at the till. No matter what customer enters the shop, she understands even from afar what he requires. Before he asks for a certain thing, she puts it into his hands. And she goes back to the till, and sits down. Another customer comes. And before he too asks for anything she puts it into his hands. She serves him, and again she seats herself at the till.

One day, two days, three days pass; always in this fashion

does she serve the customers. Twenty servants could scarcely attend to the shop, and the daughter both attends to the shop all alone and takes her place at the till, and her father does nothing but go for walks.

The daughter says: 'Father, betake yourself as an old man and go to the coffee-house, and sit down, and enter into discourse with your companions. Do not worry concerning the shop. I can look after another two shops, and nevertheless take my place at the till.'

The father went to the coffee-house. He sits down. He took up a newspaper, he is reading. There came to him a merchant, and he like himself is a trader, and so they were two merchants together. Now our merchant says to the other: 'You have servants indeed, but I would not give my daughter's little finger, and her understanding, for the whole nation.' The other merchant says: 'Is your daughter very hardworking?' Her father says: 'She is busy all day. I had twenty assistants, they attended to my shop, and they were unable to supply the needs of the customers, but my daughter alone ministers to them all, and serves them, and she takes her place at the till to boot.' The other merchant says: 'If your daughter is such a worker, and so busy, she must be worth a great deal to you. Will you lay a wager with me? Whatever I will ask of you, that shall your daughter accomplish. Let us make a contract: if your daughter brings me what I ask, I will give you from my belongings whatever I possess: my shop, my houses, my wife, and children. And whatever wares there may be, they shall all be made over to you. But should your daughter not bring what I ask, what will you give to me?' The girl's father answered: 'I will give you all I possess, both in wares and in buildings, whatever there is in the shop, and I will strip, that you may take my shirt too.' All things were agreed upon satisfactorily. A contract was made up to seven days. If within that time she has not brought the thing which the merchant asks for, he will enter the shop, and whatever there is or there is not he will take, together with the wares. 'But should she bring me that thing, then you shall come within seven days and take my shop, and all the wares in it, and my wife shall be made over to you with her children.'

72

The contract was made. The merchant betook himself, the father of the girl went off. He returned to the shop, and sat down. He put his hand to his cheek, and begins to ponder. The daughter says: 'O Father, what are you cogitating?' The father says: 'Eh, Sinko, I have eaten dung, and now I do smell of it!' The daughter said: 'How so, father?' The father answered: 'How indeed, Sinko!' He takes from his breast the contract. The girl said: 'Heigh-ho! Now he has done it!' She sighed. The girl said to her father: 'My father, have you no understanding? And do you not know that as I am a girl, if I venture out of the town, evil-doers will fall upon me, to do me mischief?' The father said: 'Eh, Sinko, I have eaten dung, and I too am repentant, but it has happened!' The girl said: 'Oh! father, the bet is his. And he will take our shop, and owing to your foolishness we shall be left in the streets, to roam about.'

One day passed, two days passed, five days passed. Two days remained. The girl asked her father: 'Father, up to how many days did you make the contract valid?' The father says: 'Up to seven days we made it.' The girl rings the telephone. She speaks to Grozda: 'Grozda, lead out the horse, and place upon him his saddle and collar. I am coming directly.'

Evening came. The girl set forth. She carried with her a box of sugar and a sack of leblebi nuts. She prepares a pot of sherbet for the horse. She gives it to the horse; he drank. She places before him the leblebi nuts; he ate. The girl arose in the middle of the night. The father is asleep. The girl says to the serving maid: 'Grozda, should my father arise, you are not to tell him.' She set out, donned a cloak, mounted the horse, and they went and they went.

She entered a wood, a forest. She walked a little on foot. One step, two steps she took. 'Sh!-sh!' sigh the leaves on the trees, and she exclaims: 'Ah! some one is coming!' Now the wind blows. She bestirred herself and said: 'I will go on. If it be His will I shall die, and if it be His will I shall remain alive.' She went and she went until half of the way was accomplished. The leaves are sighing: 'Ah!' She cries out: 'They will seize me!' She hears Bulgars, they are calling 'Dooo' to the cattle. She said: 'I will go on, and should He

73

will it, be they shepherds, cowherds, drivers or thieves, I have set out unto my death.'

She went on, and she said: 'I shall go this way, and should He will it, He will lead me on.' On and on went the girl. She cast her eyes upwards. What does she see? A man, dead, and he is hanged, and swinging. What does she see? On his hand, on the little finger, a ring is gleaming. The girl says: 'How shall I take it?' There stands under the man a horse, tied to a tree. The girl says: 'How shall I take this ring?' The horse says: 'Do you not see, you cannot take it, but climb on to my back, and reach up and then you will be able to take it. And get down again as quickly as possible, and tether me again in my place, lest my master should come from yonder road, for then he would kill both you and me. And get back whence you came as quickly as possible, and begone.' The girl bestirred herself, jumped down, mounted her own horse, gives him one stroke of the whip, and he carries her home. She returned home and dismounted. What does Grozda see? 'O my mistress has come back!' 'Quiet! do not shout. Did my father arise?' The serving-maid answers: 'He did not get up at all.' 'Quickly, take the saddle off the horse, and remove his collar and tie him up in the stable, and take a cloth to cover him, for he is sweating, and wipe him down well. And make him a pot of sherbet and place before him nuts and raisins to eat.'

Day broke. The girl went and opened the shop and there she is in her seat at the till. Whatever a customer comes to buy, without his asking, she takes it, puts it into his hands, and he departs. The father came. He sits down, deep in thought. Only one day remained; six days had passed and the seventh had come. The merchant arrived. 'Eh! how goes it with our agreement, our contract? I desire that it be fulfilled. Come now, take your daughter, and come out of the shop.' He started turning them out, did the merchant. He leads them out of the house. The girl's father says: 'Now I beseech you, give us at least the little room, that we may live in it.' The merchant answers: 'Hasten, hasten, quickly, quickly, come out, or I will strip you and take your shirt too.' The girl still continues praying and beseeching: 'Now do not treat us so. Is it not a sin?' The merchant says: 'Let

be, let be, quickly, quickly, come out, and ill-luck to you!'
The girl said: 'Wait, I beseech you, do not confiscate my
shop. What is your wager?' She called the merchant, she
called her father; witnesses came. The girl says: 'Are you
witnesses?' The men say: 'We are.' 'And you,' says the girl
to the merchant, 'what is your wager with my father?' The
merchant answered: 'Your father knows.' The girl says: 'Ha!
my father knows! You found that my father was a simpleton,
and you made a wager with him.' She thrusts her hand into
her pocket and she took out the ring. 'Is this your wager?'
The merchant gasped 'Ah!' and fell down dead. And she
approaches the dead man and sets about stripping him, so
that she may take even his shirt.

The whole town assembled about the head of the dead
man. Two thieves heard of it, the chief and another thief.
They came to the capital. They heard that a man was dead.
'Now let us go and see who is this man that is dead.' The
thieves went. From this person they make enquiries, from
that person they get information. 'What did this fellow die
of?' 'It happened thus, there is a maiden here, a merchant's
daughter. The father laid a wager that she should go to a
certain place. There she found a man hanging, a ring on his
finger, and the girl brought it and showed it to the merchant,
and he fell down dead.' The chief of the thieves asks: 'And
where is this girl?' A Bulgar answers: 'See now, in the Ulitsa
Legue there is a shop, and she is sitting inside it.' The chief
and the robber went there.

'Good day, mistress!' 'God greet you, merchant!' 'Will you
give me some of that cloth! How much money do you want?'
'Two hundred levs.' He went off, they both departed, and
wended their way home. And as they go they converse together: 'Well, fancy now, and so it was a woman who came
and took that ring!' They went back yonder. They say to the
other thieves: 'We have found the ring on a girl, a merchant's
daughter, and she sits in the shop.' The chief says: 'To-
morrow we will go there again.' They went to her. 'Good
evening, mistress!' 'The Lord greet you kindly!' They bar-
gained for some cloth, bought it, and ask her: 'How much
money do you want?' 'I want from you three hundred levs.'
They took out their money to pay the sum. They gave her

two hundred levs, and as for the remaining hundred, they tell her they have not got enough: 'Will you trust us till to-morrow?' They took the cloth and departed.

The girl rings the telephone. 'Grozda, in the evening harness the pony-chaise and wait for me on the road.' The girl closed the shop, went home, saw the thieves in the street, and says to Grozda: 'Do you see yonder men who are driving in the chaise? You must drive our chaise behind them: quietly, quietly, always behind them, whithersoever they go, you also must always follow.' They went on and on into a wood.

The girl got down. 'Grozda, you must wait for me here to-night, until the seventh hour. If I am alive, I will come. If I die, you must wait until the seventh hour. As soon as the seventh hour has passed, you will know that I am dead, and you must harness the chaise and depart. The merchant's daughter set off, quietly, quietly, behind them, on foot; whithersoever they go, thither she follows always behind them secretly. They went and they went till they came to a trap-door. They raised the trap-door, and descended. The girl bestirs herself, follows and raises the trap-door. What does she see? Steps all the way down. The girl says: 'I will go down, and God give what fortune He may!' She descended, and what does she see? Through the doorway forty thieves asleep, and they are all snoring. The girl said: 'I will enter, and let it be as God wills.' She opens the door and steps in among the thieves. Now the thieves' door, when you open it, opens quietly, but when you shut it, creaks with all its might—'paaat!' creaks the door. The door creaked, but they heard not.

She went on and on. What does she see? Through the doorway the chief is lying asleep, and at the head of his bed-stead a watch is hanging. His revolver is hung up at his head. The girl makes a movement forward, snatches the watch and the revolver. The maiden then starts to go out. Just as she passes out, the door creaked and all the thieves heard; the girl took fright. Whither shall she turn? She opens a door. What does she see? A heap of slain men in the room. She casts herself among them, hides herself in their blood. The thieves fall asleep again. The girl arises, comes out, and started to return home. The thieves have a small dog. It started barking at the girl. The thieves arose: 'Heavens, there is some one outside!' Quickly the thieves arise, and they gave chase and ran outside. The girl climbs a tree, and hides herself among the leaves. The small dog went up to the tree and barks at her. The thieves say: 'Gemini! Twice this small dog has awaked us.' 'Wait, I will slay it.' One of them took out his revolver, fired, killed it. The thieves went below again. The girl climbs down, and returned to Grozda.

Grozda saw her. 'Heigh! mistress! Has anyone wounded you? You are so blood-stained!' 'Quick, harness the chaise, and let us begone.' They went home, she stripped, put on other clothes. She goes and opens the shop, and takes her seat. Come the thieves: 'Good day, mistress.' 'God greet you, master.' They bought cloth, they ask her: 'How much do you want?' 'I want from you five hundred levs.' The thieves take out the money, pay it. The girl says: 'Be seated here; you are merchants. For all the bargains you have struck with me I should be grateful and will send you a present for your wife.' 'Grozda,' she calls on the telephone, 'take a box and enclose the revolver in it, and take another box and put the watch in it and bring them to the shop.' 'See here,' says she to the thief, 'this is for your wife, with many, many greetings from me. Take her this as a gift from me. And much health to your comrade's wife; take her this from me as a present.'

They went and they went. The chief says: 'Heavens! a fine girl that, and clever.' They went home. What do they see when they open the box? 'Good heavens, my revolver!' And when they open the other box: 'Good heavens, my watch! But this is my watch and my revolver! Bravo, and long life and love to this woman, for she came and stole my revolver and my watch! Now how shall we manage to kill her?'

One thief bestirred himself, put on a tar-seller's clothes. He went to her with a load of oil. He went to the shop: 'Good day, mistress!' 'The Lord greet you, tar-man!' 'I have a little oil which perhaps you would like to buy? Forty loads have I, and the oil therefrom.' The girl said: 'For how much money will you sell me the oil?' 'Five and a half levs the kilo.' 'When will you bring it?' 'By to-morrow morning, mistress, I will be in the shop.' The thief went back to his comrades. He loaded forty loads, all the thieves in the forty barrels, he hid one thief a-piece in each of the forty barrels. He brings her the oil. He came in the morning. 'Good morrow, mistress.' He brings the oil. 'Where shall we unload the oil?' The girl says: 'Yonder, in the yard.'

They unloaded all the oil in the yard. The first barrel is full of oil, and she thinks that all contain oil. Mid-day came. The tar-man says: 'Mistress, you want to go off to dinner and I want to go off to dinner. At what time will you return to the shop, that we may measure the oil?' The girl says: 'Come at two o'clock at the latest.'

Two o'clock came. Grozda is in the shop, alone. She took a needle. She much desires to taste a little oil on her bread. She pierces the barrel. The thieves say: 'Shall we get out?' Grozda says, 'Mistress, see yonder in the courtyard, I went with a needle, I had just pierced a barrel in order to take a little oil to eat with my bread, when these fellows call to me: "Shall we get out?"' and I answered: "Remain".'

The merchant's daughter says: 'Be silent, do not shout!' She speaks through the telephone, the police inspector comes and the sergeants and the policemen. 'See here, in my court-yard forty thieves, all in barrels, are concealing themselves and awaiting their opportunity to kill us.' The police take out their knives; they surrounded all the barrels with bared knives, the thieves in the centre, the police all around on the outside. At their head one policeman pierces a barrel. The thief says: 'Shall we come out?' The policeman answers: 'Come out.' And as each of the forty thieves comes out, the police with their knives kill the whole forty, one by one. Remained the tar-seller. Him too they seize, lead him out into the street, set him on fire, which consumes him. He is burned to ashes.

16. The Chordilenjis

There was a king and that king had three sons and three daughters. The time came for him to die. He left a command to his children; they were to give their sisters in marriage to whomsoever should ask for them, and not to refuse anyone.

The king fell dead. The three brothers said: 'Let us each take our own horse, and go a-wandering.' Said the youngest brother: 'Let us first marry off our sisters, and then we will set forth.'

For the eldest sister there came a wolf. The eldest brother said: 'I will not give her.' The second brother said: 'I too will not give her.' The youngest brother said: 'O Brothers! My father left us a command; I will not break it.' The youngest brother gave his sister. For the second sister there came a bear. The eldest brother gave not, the second brother gave not, the youngest brother gave. For the youngest there came an eagle, he who flies swiftly. The eldest brother gave not, the second brother gave not, the youngest brother gave. 'Now', said he, 'the time has come for each of us to mount his horse and go a-wandering.'

The eldest brother said: 'O Brothers! Let us set forth. Perhaps my youngest brother feels annoyed with us.' They mounted their horses, and went on and on until they came to a meadow. They alighted there; one brother puts up the tent, and another collects bits of half-burnt wood so that they may each have a drink of coffee. They sat down to eat their evening meal. Then a certain Chordilenjis appeared. He said: '*Amán*, O Brothers! become my father and my brother! Give me a piece of bread, for I have eaten nothing for three days and three nights.' The eldest brother said: 'I have started out on a journey, and have brought only enough for myself to eat.' The second brother also gave nothing to the beggar. Said the youngest brother: 'Give him my share to-night, I will not eat.'

Evening fell. They prepare to keep watch. The eldest brother placed the table before him, lit the lantern at his head, and hung it up to give him light. He placed his knife in front of him, he placed his book in front of him, and he began to read. Suddenly a monster appears from the back of beyond. It says: 'Arise, and tell me what this road is, for I have lost my way.' The boy answers: 'I too do not know this road and this mountain, nor where they lead. Since I fell from my mother's womb, I have been a-wandering.' Said the monster: 'Arise, show me, or I will eat you.' The boy answered: 'Either you will eat me, or you will not be able to;'

79

and the monster hurled himself at him, to devour him. The boy drew his knife and cut off the monster's head. He took the two ears and put them into his sack. Day broke. He went to his brothers and woke them; but he did not tell them that a monster had appeared to him.

Night fell. They sat down to their evening meal. Yonder comes the Chordilenjis: '*Amán*, Brothers! For three days I have eaten nothing. This evening also give me a morsel to eat.' The eldest brother gave not, the second brother gave not, the youngest brother said: 'This evening also give him my share; I will not eat.' The eldest brother said: 'O my Brother! if you give this fellow of your bread, he will do us some devilry.' The youngest brother answered: '*Eholla!* if he does I will give him a blow, and close his mouth.'

Evening fell. The second brother prepares to keep watch. He too placed the table before him, lit the lantern at his head, hung it up, placed his knife in front of him, placed the book in front of him, and began to read. From the back of beyond appears a two-headed monster. It says to him: 'Arise, and show me where this road and this mountain lead, for I have lost my way.' '*Te girimi kirimi!* Since I fell from my mother's womb I have been a-wandering; I too know nothing about this road and this mountain, nor where they lead.' Said the monster: 'Either arise and tell me, or I will eat you.' The youth answered: 'Either you will eat me, or you will be unable to.' The monster casts himself upon him: the boy draws his knife and cuts off the monster's two heads. He takes the four ears and puts them in his sack. Day broke. He approached his brothers, woke them, and they had a chat together.

Evening fell. They sat down to eat their evening meal. Behold yonder comes the Chordilenjis once more! The eldest brother gave not, the second brother gave not, the youngest brother said: 'O, Brothers! Give him my share to-night again. I will not eat: let him eat.' The eldest brother said: 'O Brother mine! You wish to give this fellow of your bread, but he will do us some devilry.' The youngest brother said: '*Eholla!* if he does I will give him a blow, and close his mouth.'

Night fell. The youngest boy prepares to keep watch. He lit his lantern, hung it up at his head, placed the table in front of him, placed the knife in front of him, placed the book in front of him, and began to read. Behold from the back of beyond appears a three-headed monster. It said to him: 'Arise, show me where this road and this mountain lead.' Said the boy: '*Te girimi kirimi!* Since I fell from my mother's womb I have been a-wandering; I too know nothing about this road and this mountain.' Said the monster: 'Either arise and show me, or I will eat you.' The boy answered: 'Either you will eat me, or you will be unable to.' The monster hurled himself at him, to eat him; the youth draws his knife, cuts off the three heads, takes the six ears, and places them in his sack. In drawing his knife he cuts the lantern-rope. The lantern fell, and went out. Now he thinks to himself: 'Dear me! If I go and fetch a match, my brothers will wake and say: "Is that the little one who has seen something to frighten him, and has grown afraid and extinguished the lantern?" ' So he cast his eyes around, and there in front of him a fire was shining. He took the lantern and made his way towards the fire.

He came upon an old woman. Quoth he to the old woman: 'O Old Woman! what are you doing here?' The old woman answered: 'See, Sinko, I am drawing in the night and spinning out the light.' 'Spin out the night, old woman, and draw in the light.' The old woman spun out the night and drew in the light so that 'one eye could not be seen by the other'. He bound the old woman to a tree. 'There, old woman, I will bind you to a tree while I go and light my lantern.' He went to his lantern. What does he see? Forty-one thieves are lying around the fire, and on that fire is a cauldron, with forty-one rams cooking in it. He lit his lantern, and started to make his way back; he came on and on until he had covered half the distance, when he bethought him: 'Heavens! I have no right to this fire!' So he blew out the flame and extinguished his lantern. Then he went back and woke them all. The thieves see him. 'What are you seeking here? No one comes here! How were you brave enough to come?' 'Behold my bravery!' And with his two little fingers he lifts the cauldron from the tripod, sets it down on the ground, lifts it up again with his two little fingers, and places it back on the tripod. The thieves said: 'Heigh! Now we are

men, and you are a man. We are struggling to get possession
of three beautiful girls. For forty years we have been unable
to get them. Now you, a man, have appeared, and here are
we, also men; now we shall be able to seize them.'

Now they made ready to go. They went on and on till they
came to a large building. Now the thieves ask one another:
'How shall we seize the girls? How shall we get hold of them?'
'I will tell you,' says the boy. 'Bring me forty nails.' He hammered all the nails into the wall, up to the top. 'Come now!
I will descend inside; you must bind me with a rope, and let
yourselves down one by one.' They let one thief down: he
killed him. One by one he killed the whole forty. There remained the chief: he kills him too.

He went on, opened the door, and looked inside. One of
the girls is sleeping. He drank water, ate Turkish delight, and
took her for his eldest brother. He went round to another
door, and opened it upon the second sister. He ate Turkish
delight, drank water, and took her for his second brother. He
went on to the youngest sister, opened the door, entered,
drank sherbet, kissed her between the eyebrows and took her
for himself. Now the eldest sister said: 'What are you looking
for here? No one comes here; but if my aunt sees you, she will
eat you.' And the three sisters said: 'See that you get us out
of here as quickly as possible, for our aunt will come and eat
you.' The youth said: 'Come! I will go and wake my brothers;
dress yourselves as quickly as possible; I will return.'

He hurried off straightway to the old woman. The old
woman saw him. 'Be quick, Sinko, for I am freezing; I shall
die.' 'I will untie you, but you must draw in the night very
slowly, and spin out the light, for you were drawing in the
night too quickly, and spinning out the light; but do it very
gradually and I will leave you. Should you make broad daylight come too soon, wheresoever you go, I will find you and
kill you.'

Then he went back to his brothers and woke them. 'Ha,
Brothers! Collect our belongings and let us mount our horses
and set off together: I have found three sisters, and we will
take them for ourselves.' They journeyed on and on until
they came to the sisters. The youngest brother alighted. He
takes the eldest girl, throws her behind his eldest brother; he

takes the second girl, throws her behind his second brother; he takes his own maiden, the youngest, and throws her behind himself—and they start afresh.

They went on and on. Behold the Chordilenjis seizes the youngest brother's maiden. The eldest brother said: 'Did I not tell you, Brother, he would do us some devilry? But you, what did you say? "*Eholla!* if he does I will give him a blow and close his mouth."' The youngest brother says: 'Well, Brothers! May you remain in health! Now depart, for I am going to turn back.'

He returned to his eldest sister. His sister saw him: 'Heee! Brother! You gave me to a wolf; he will come now and eat you.' She gives him a blow, and turns him into a broom, and casts him on one side. The wolf comes along: 'Oh! Ho! Wife! I smell meat!' '*Eholla!*' the wife answers, 'you have just been eating men, and the moment you see me you want to eat me too!' Now she says: 'If my eldest brother were to come, what would you do to him?' 'First I would eat him, then I would void him.' 'But my second brother?' 'Him too would I eat!' 'But the youngest?' 'Up to my head I have room for him, he will always be welcome.' She gives the broom a blow and turns it into a man again. Says the wolf: 'What do you want, that you have come here?' The boy answers: 'Behold, it is like this: the Chordilenjis has carried off my maiden.' 'Heigh! We will fight him day and night, and, if I find him, I will eat him. You must now go to your sister, the wife of the eagle.'

He went to her. His sister saw him and began to cry. 'O Brother! You gave me to an eagle, and if he comes he will claw you and tear out your eyes.' She gives him a blow, and turns him into a needle and pins him to her breast. The eagle comes: 'Oh! Ho! wife! I smell man's flesh.' Says the girl: '*Eholla!* You have just been clawing men, and, the moment you come and see me, you want to tear and claw me also. If my eldest brother were to come, what would you do to him?' 'I would tear out his two eyes and place them in your hands.' 'But if my second brother were to come?' 'To him I would do the same also.' 'And if my youngest brother were to come?' 'For him I have room up to my head! He will always be welcome.' She gave the needle a blow, and turned it into a man again. 'But you, why have you come here?' 'Well! it is like this: the Chordilenjis has carried off my wife.' 'Heigh! Don't you have anything to do with him, or he will do you harm. He can fly twice as fast as I can. If I found him I would tear out his two eyes, and make him blind for ever.'

He then goes to his other sister. And she exclaims: 'Heee! Brother! You gave me to a bear, and, if he comes, he will eat you.' She gives him a blow, and turns him into an apple, and places it on the shelf. The bear came: '*Holelay!* I smell men!' The wife says: '*Eholla!* you have just been eating men, and now you come and want to eat me too! Should my eldest brother come, what would you do to him?' 'First I would eat him, then I would void him.' 'But the second?' 'Him too would I eat, and then void.' 'But the youngest?' 'Up to my head there is room for him: he will always be welcome.' The sister gives the apple a blow and turns it into a man. The bear asks him: 'But you, why have you come here?' 'Well, it is like this: the Chordilenjis has carried off my wife.' 'Heigh! We will fight him night and day. And if we find him, we will break him all to pieces. But you, do you know what you must do? You must take your horse—see yonder, there are big gates. You must spur on your horse, and pass through at full speed, for as soon as the doors clang to they will kill you as well as your horse. There, on the right-hand side, there is a stable and in it a collar. And whatever horse comes along and places his head through it, on him you must fasten that collar.'

The youth's maiden sees him; he beckons to her with his head, and up she comes. He mounts the horse, throws her behind him and carries off his maiden. They rode on and on. The horse neighs: 'Master, master! The lady has gone!' The Chordilenjis asks: 'At what time?' 'Five o'clock.' The Chordilenjis says: 'Let him go, even if 'twere six o'clock.' The Chordilenjis mounts his mare, gives her one shout, and overtakes the lady. 'Listen to me,' says he to the boy, 'I have eaten of your bread; for three nights I caused you to remain hungry. I forgive you. But the next time, as soon as you appear, I will kill you.' Then he seized the maiden and carried her back to his home.

Now the boy returned to the bear and said: 'I went to the

place and carried off my maiden; but the Chordilenjis over-
took me and said to me: "I ate your bread three nights and
caused you to remain hungry. I forgive you. But the next time
as soon as you appear, I will kill you."' The bear said: 'Now
do not go and sacrifice your head for the sake of a girl!' But
the boy replied: 'I shall go, and if he chooses he can kill me.'
'Well! go if you must, but as soon as you enter the gates you
will find a colt, and, if you can, seize it, otherwise you can do
nothing.'

The boy seized the colt, put on its bridle, mounted it, took
the maiden and threw her behind him. He gives one shout to
the horse. But the mare in the stable, the mother of the colt,
neighs: 'Master, master! The lady has gone!' 'At what time?'
'No time remains!' *Breholla!* Is it true?' The Chordilenjis
mounts his mare. Now this way, now that, he tries to overtake them, but he cannot. The mare neighs to her colt:
'Heigh, Sinko! I will impose upon you an obligation. How
is it you drank my milk and yet you do not shake yourself
and cause the boy to fall, and make mincemeat of him?' The
colt hears, shakes itself, and makes mincemeat of the boy.
The Chordilenjis takes him, collects the pieces, places them
in his saddle-bags, takes the boy's horse and throws him across
its back, and the horse straightway gallops off to his sister,
the wife of the eagle.

The youngest sister sees him and weeps. The eagle hurries
off. There is in some miraculous place some miraculous
water from a well near Mecca. As the bird stoops to get a
little water he knocks himself and breaks his wing. He returns, sprinkles the water over the boy. 'Achoo!' said the boy.
'I have been sleeping.' 'You have slept well indeed! The
Chordinlenjis has outwitted you disastrously! Eat and drink
to me, for I went and fetched the water of life, and see, see
how I have broken my wing solely for your sake!'

There is the tale! Here is your health!

SERBO-BOSNIAN

Recorded by Professor Rade Uhlik

17. Men Born of Fishes

There was once a certain rich man and he had no children at all. One day he caught a big fish. And that fish asked him: 'What wilt thou do with me?' And he answered: 'I'll fry you and I'll eat you.' The fish said to him: 'Put me aside from those other fish, and when thou reachest home give one piece to thy wife, one to the bitch, and one to the mare, and hang up the fish-bones to dry.'

He arrived home and when he had done everything exactly as the fish had bidden him, his wife, the bitch, and the mare became pregnant. In course of time they brought forth their young. The wife bore twin sons, the bitch twin puppies, and the mare twin foals.

When, after a little time the boys grew up, they said to their father: 'Father, pray let us travel about the world a little, so that we may get to know other men.' Their father said to them: 'I will allow you, but neither of you has a saddle for the horse.' So their father set to and put on his shoes and climbed to the top of the house to seek for saddles. But when he raised his head towards the roof he saw two struts jutting out like saddles, and said, 'Go, climb up, take down the saddles, and get the horses ready for the journey.' Whereupon they made ready, took their dogs with them, and set forth.

Journeying thus, they came to a river and said one to another: 'Let us go to that bridge yonder and part there from one another. Let us make our marks on the bridge, so that when we return it will be known which of us is alive and which dead.' They cut their marks on the bridge in two places and made this pact together: 'From whichever of the marked spots blood is flowing, he who made the mark is killed.' And so they parted from one another.

The elder brother, as he wandered on his way, saw a fire far off. When he drew near he found a mill on the spot. There he stopped and passed the night. In the morning he started on his travels again and came to a town where black flags were hoisted. There the people did not dare to light a candle by night, nor to utter a word, such terror was upon them. He entered a coffee-house, ate his supper, fed the mare and the bitch and passed the night in a room.

When day dawned, he said to the master of the house: 'I am going to-day to the forest, but my horse will remain here.' He took the bitch and set off for the forest. Journeying thus, he came to a big hollow rock. And when he drew near to it, there suddenly arose a dreadful three-headed snake, and stretched itself out to devour him. But he drew his sword and cut off one of its heads, then he pulled out its tongue and wrapped it up and put it into his pocket, and returned to the coffee-house. The innkeeper asked him: 'Didst thou kill anything at all to-day in the forest?' And he answered: 'I am not used to thy mountains and I could catch nothing.' He slept the night there again and in the morning went back to the forest. When the snake again lifted up its head to devour him, he cut off its second head also. On the third day he cut off its third head, and hid the tongues on his own person.

When he had gone some distance from that spot, a certain Gypsy came along, found the three heads without tongues, brought them to the King and said: 'Behold, your daughter has been stopping in the den of snakes, and I cut off the heads of that snake, of that dragon which carried off your daughter.' They went, released the girl and gave her to this Gypsy.

But all this affair weighed on the mind of the innkeeper, and he went to the King and said to him: 'At our house there is a beautiful unknown man from a foreign land. He was three days in the forest, and each time he returned to me he brought nothing back, nor told me aught. But nevertheless I think that something has happened to him.'

The King summoned the unknown man to a feast of honour. When the man saw those three heads, he said: 'Bring me hither those three heads!' Then he opened the mouths of the heads and asked: 'Where are the tongues from these heads?'

87

And the Gypsy said: 'They had no tongues.' And the man pulled those three tongues from his pocket and put them into their right places. Now the King saw that it was not the Gypsy who had killed the snake but the unknown man, and he wanted to slay the Gypsy. But the stranger said to the King: 'Do not kill him, but fasten him up in prison until our wedding has passed by. And later on let us give him a hundred ducats and set him free that he may go away alive and well. Because, even thou, O King, if thou hadst found those heads, wouldst also have taken them.'

When the stranger was tucked up to sleep with the girl, a shadowy light appeared to him. He asked the girl: 'What is that?' She answered: 'Nothing good.' Then he got ready and started to go towards that fire. So he travelled the whole day and before night arrived at the spot and found a graveyard there. When night came on and he could go no farther, he kindled a fire for himself in order to pass the night on the spot. Glancing around on all sides, he saw some stones shaped like a human being, a dog, and a horse. Then somebody called from above, from the tree: 'Let me warm myself, I am chilled.' And he answered: 'Come down and warm thyself.' But the little old grandam said: 'I dare not because of thy dog: here is a hair for thee, bind him!' He threw it over the dog and bound him. And that old beldam came down from the tree, and striking around with her wand turned him, his horse and his dog into stone. When the King perceived that his son-in-law had not returned he again put on mourning clothes.

Meanwhile the other brother returned to the bridge to see what was the matter with his twin. When he saw his brother's mark oozing blood his heart grew heavy. He started off again on his travels and came to that mill where his brother also had slept. The miller asked him: 'Where hast thou tarried for so many days?' 'I was in the forest and stopped there.'

When day dawned the youth started as early as possible to go farther in search of his brother. So he came to that landlord where his brother also had passed the night. Then the innkeeper said to him: 'Where hast thou been, brother? Thou didst take a wife from here and disappeared somewhere. Therefore now black flags are hoisted.' Then the innkeeper hurried off to the King and said to him: 'Lo! your son-in-law has returned!'

Meanwhile the youth himself also arrived and they began kissing him. For his sister-in-law too thought that this was her husband, and she kissed him; but he would not kiss her. So this son-in-law perceived that his brother was away yonder, and that this was his sister-in-law, and he would not kiss her. When night came, he went into the bedroom with his sister-in-law. She began to draw near to him but he said: 'Do not come near me or I will slay thee.' Then she told her mother about this. Her mother said: 'Leave him alone to-night! He has been for so many days in the forest that he is tired.' Meantime there appeared to him also a shadowy light, and he asked his sister-in-law: 'What is that?' She replied: 'I told thee before that he who goes to the spot where that light is shining never comes back.'

Whereupon he rose from his bed, mounted his horse and went away. So he also reached the graveyard. And that little old woman called out again, as she had to his brother, that she was cold, and she gave him also a hair with which to bind the dog. But he cast it on the fire. Then the old woman began to draw near to him in order to touch him with her wand, but the dog caught her. And he turned and seized the axe in his hand and now he struck at the old woman. But she cried to him: 'Do not slay me and I will restore thy brother to life. Here! do thou take this wand and wave it about thee and say aloud: "As thou wast man before, so be again."' When he touched the stone with that wand his brother became alive, and exclaimed: 'How sweetly have I slept, why didst thou awaken me?' Then he restored to life also his dog and his horse. Then the two dogs and the two brothers hurled themselves on that old beldam and made mincemeat of her. And they took the wand and went from stone to stone, struck each of them and restored them to life one by one.

When the King saw so many people approaching him he grew afraid and said: 'There comes my son-in-law with the soldiers. Spread two carpets, one for strife and one for peace.' And the soldiers began to step on to the peace carpet. When his son-in-law and his brother arrived, the King and his wife began kissing them. And the King's daughter also jumped to her feet, and when she kissed her husband he also kissed her back. But when she kissed her husband's brother, he did not kiss her. So they made a great banquet for a whole week.

Then they said to the King: 'We have a father and mother, and it behoves us to go to see them.' The King answered: 'Do not go, son-in-law: when I die thou shalt become King and thy brother will be beside thee.' But they said: 'We must go, and if thou givest us thy daughter it is well, but if not what can we do?' The King gave them many ducats and they departed with the girl.

Journeying home in this manner, the first brother regarded his twin with jealous eyes because he had passed a night with his wife. Meanwhile they arrived at a great river with a bridge. And he was so enraged that he pushed his brother into the water to drown. When he had recovered his senses a little, this murderous brother cried out: 'O Golden God, what have I done to my brother? He restored me to life, and I have cast him into the water.' And from that same spot he pushed his wife also into the river, and sprang after them himself. And the terrible fishes devoured them.

And it happened thus to them. They were born of fishes, and into fishes they returned. And so there are in fish four bodily parts: the human, the dog's, the horse's, and the fish's. Their mouth is like a dog's, their head like a horse's, their front fins like human hands, and their back parts like those of a fish.

18. Baldhead's Cannibal Sister

There was a rich man, and he had nine sons, but had not a single daughter. His wife was pregnant, and she looked after the neat cattle. She said within herself: 'God, Golden God, grant that I get a little girl!' As she said this she saw a beautiful heifer. The wife begged God that she might at least have a little girl like that small heifer. She returned to her house, and sure enough next morning she bore a little girl. But see! what does she resemble? with slender little feet, the head of an ox, and teeth as big as a pig's and like the hooks of a balance! She had a youngest son who was bald-headed and not right in his mind. They all considered him a little foolish.

They had many fat and fleshy sheep. The following day, when they came in the morning to inspect the flock, one sheep had its neck cut and lay dead on the ground. And thenceforward, from day to day at dawn, they used to find a sheep slain. They could in no wise find out who was doing this to their sheep. Therefore they agreed one with the other to watch the sheep each night, first one and then another brother. But nevertheless in the morning they always found a sheep slain. The brothers could not catch the rascal who did this to their sheep.

Afterwards that bald-headed brother of theirs, Chelo, spoke to his father, his mother and his brothers: 'Well, then! let me go one night to guard the sheep.' But those other brothers said to him: 'How couldst thou go, thou fool? We who are so wise could not find anything; and thou, so brainless, wilt thou catch anything? But thou canst go if thou wilt. But thou must know that the same thing will happen with thee.'

And Baldhead went and slept the whole day. And that night he took an axe in his hands and crept among the sheep, and hid among them. When midnight approached, from the other side there sprang over the hedge among the sheep that little girl who was born with the ox-head and the big teeth. With the utmost speed she twisted the head of a sheep and tore it off with her teeth. Baldhead was clever and strikes her with the axe on the flank and hip. She was frightened, sprang back over the hedge and fled. Baldhead now is for going home, but does not dare to go, he fears lest this girl may return among the sheep.

When morning came Baldhead went home. There his brothers asked him: 'What didst thou do this night, Baldhead, since again this night a sheep was eaten?' Baldhead says to them: 'Mother, sweetest, mayest thou live to old age! I will tell thee truly who strangles our sheep. Lo! it is that little sister of ours whom thou didst bear.' But his mother was angry at his words: 'Thou, my unhappy child, thou canst not look at this thy one and only little sister, whom I bore, without wanting to kill her. Get thee gone from this place, thou shalt not stay with me any more, vanish to any spot thou knowest, that I may not set eyes on thee any more!' And his other brothers too rose up in anger against him, because he had wounded his sister in the hip with his axe. And he says to all his family: 'As she devours our sheep, so she will devour you too, every one of you. See! I will go away, I will take my little horse and my two little dogs, and you may give me as much as you will.'

After that he took all that belonged to him and departed from them. He goes on and on for many days, and travelling thus he came to a big hollow rock and sat himself down to rest a little. When midnight approached he trembled a little from fear of what might happen to him. And suddenly God willed that the hollow rock—that rocky cave—should open, and there arose from it a sound as though someone were calling from within. Baldhead answered and entered. And there inside that cave appeared before him a lovely girl. She asked him whether he would like to take her as his wife. And he took her, and remained happily with her for a year.

After that there came into his, Baldhead's, mind the memory of his father, and he grew anxious about his mother and his brothers. He was all for going to see them, because a heavy burden lay upon his soul. For a whole week he could neither eat nor drink from sorrow. His wife asked him: 'What ails thee, that thou dost neither eat nor drink?' And he told her all that was the matter. And she said: 'How would it be if we were to go to see how things are with them up yonder?' So he climbed up from the house to go to his relations, and said to his wife: 'If the dogs bark, set them loose. They will know that some kind of trouble has come to me, and they will find me wheresoever I am. Do not forget.'

So he set out along the road on his journey. When he arrived near his former old home, he found no one alive of his family, and no one in the village who remained after he had left. That little sister of his, who had grown three metres, had devoured them all. He came to his sister, and she pretended to wait upon him attentively. She said to him: 'Come near to me, sit down; I will go, brother Baldhead, to make coffee for thee.'

Then she went off to the place where his horse was tied

up, struck down the horse and ate one of its feet, and returned indoors to her brother saying to him: 'How is this, brother? thou didst arrive on a horse which has only three feet?' He knew what might happen to him and said: 'I arrived just so, sister.' And again she said she would go and make coffee; and she ate the second foot of the horse, and came back saying: 'Brother, thou didst not count correctly before, thou didst come on a horse with only two feet.' At that Baldhead's bowels melted with horror. In his soul he was aware of his fate and that he could not escape. The chamber was full of the bones of his mother and his brothers, whom she had devoured and gnawed to bits. His sister said to him: 'Thy sister is going to bring thee some coffee.' And she acted thus until she had devoured the whole horse.

And when she went to eat the horse, he was clever and filled his pockets, his drawers, and his bosom with the ashes from the coals, and he went up to the top of the house. She came in, did not find her brother there, and called out: 'I know where thou art, I have devoured all the men, and thy horse, and now I will devour thee also.' And she started to go upstairs to him. But he took a handful of ashes and emptied them into her eyes. She burst out crying. When she had wiped her eyes she began once more to pursue him. So each time he threw the ashes in her eyes as long as he had any ashes left.

When he had no more ashes he sprang up on to the roof of the house. And she climbed up to where he was. Now in front of the house were three great, lofty trees, and thereupon he quickly sprang on to a tree. And she said: 'Thou wilt not escape me here.' Then she jumped down beneath the tree where he was, and with her teeth she scratches and digs round about the tree. Seeing that she is about to fell that tree, he sprang on to another. When the tree fell she ran along the branches thinking that he had fallen with the tree. Seeing that he is not below she began to dig round the second tree. So she felled the second tree also.

When she was about to fell the third, Baldhead's dogs were heard as they rushed up to him barking. His heart grew light, and he called to them: 'Seize her, Arslan, seize her, Kaplan, but do not tear her to bits till I come down.' He climbed

93

down and said to his sister: 'See, sister, thou didst devour all the people in this village, and thou didst want to devour me too, but thou wilt never devour anybody any more.' Then the dogs tore her into little pieces. And he set off with his dogs and returned again to his wife.

19. The Dead Man's Gratitude

There was a certain poor Gypsy, and he had nothing anywhere. So by doing his work he earned twenty pence, and with this money he set out to seek another job. He put into his pocket three apples, and set forth to cross the mountain. And on the way there met him a certain person and asked him: 'Whither art thou going?' And he replied: 'I am going to seek work.' 'Then can I too go with thee?' And he said: 'Thou canst.' So as they were walking along his companion became thirsty, and they had no water at all. But the poor man pulled out an apple and gave it to his companion to divide it in half, into two pieces. Then he cut a small piece for himself and gave his friend the larger half of the apple. Afterwards the poor man said to his companion: 'Do thou go by one road and I will go by the other.'

So going on further, the poor man came to a cemetery. There he found a certain merchant who was taking out the bones of the dead from a tomb and, by grinding them, was reducing them to small pieces on a stone. He asked this merchant: 'Why dost thou dig up this dead man's bones, and why art thou smashing them thus on the stone?' And the merchant answered: 'He owed me twenty pence.' Whereupon the poor man gave him his own twenty pence and said to him: 'Put those bones back into the tomb and don't break them up any more.'

Then the poor man began to set off without a single penny. And once again a stranger appeared before him, asking him: 'Where art thou going? And can I too go with thee?' And the poor man pulled out the second apple and gave it to him to take away his thirst. He cut the apple into two halves and they ate it.

So journeying on they came to a town and heard someone proclaiming: 'He who will spend the night with the King's daughter, to him the King will give her.' And that companion of his sends him to spend the night with her. And he was not willing, because he had learnt that whosoever sleeps with her is found dead at her side the next morning. And his companion said again: 'Thou must go! And we have made this agreement that what we get we will divide as brothers between us.'

So they two went and announced themselves to the King. The King let the poor man alone go to sleep with her, but did not let his companion in. But his companion feared what would happen to the poor man, and therefore dug a hole and got into the room secretly. When the poor man seized the girl in his embrace to kiss her, a snake began to come out of her mouth to devour him. But that hidden companion of his drew his knife and cut off the snake's head. And that poor man who was in bed with her did not notice anything. And his companion again withdrew from them. Meanwhile the poor man began to squeeze the girl in his embrace, kissing her. And once more another snake stretched forth its head from her throat to devour him. His companion springs up and cuts off that snake's head too. When he had done this also for the third time, he put those three snakes' heads into a small bag and went out of that bedroom. And the poor man stayed, spent the night with the girl, and remained alive.

In the morning when the King opened the door of the room, he found the man whole and well. Now the King becomes light of heart, since hitherto many men had been killed spending the night with his daughter. He made a great wedding-feast because he had got a son-in-law. He asked the poor man: 'Wilt thou stop with us if I build thee a beautiful house?' The poor man was willing, but his companion did not let him stop. The King gave him his daughter and many purses of ducats for the journey. Then they set off for the place whence they had come.

When they reached those tombs where he had paid for the dead man's bones, his companion made him stop, saying: 'Stay! do not go any further; here will we divide what we have gained.' So they divided first of all the ducats. After that his companion said: 'See now, we will divide this girl too.' And the poor man said: 'We will cut her in half, then one half will be for thee, and the other for me.' The King's son-in-law was sorry to cut her in two. But his companion said: 'There is no other way, for we must keep to our agreement.'

After that he drew his sword and called out to his friend: 'Hold her by the right foot and the right hand, and I will seize her from the other side.' And when he raised his sword a headless snake fell out of her mouth. So twice more he drew his sword against her, and then also those two other snakes fell out of her. So the girl was healed and remained without snakes.

Now his companion said to the poor man: 'Look now, thou hast both the ducats and the girl in return for thy last pence which thou gavest for my bones. And see those three snakes, the three of them would have eaten thee if I had not come that night when thou didst spend the night with the King's daughter. Lo, now they are thine! so carry off all that, and remain with God!'

So they parted there, one from the other. His companion again climbed into his tomb, and the man went home and remained happy with his wife.

Recorded by Dr Alexander Petrović

20. The Church of Cheese

It happened long ago when the Gypsies had their own king. At that time the Gypsies had a church of stone and the Serbians a church of cheese. Once a Serbian visited a Gypsy: 'Listen, fellow', said he, 'let us change: I will give thee my church of cheese and do thou give me thy church of stone.' The Gypsy looks at the church of cheese and says: 'Listen, Serb, how can I give thee my church which is of stone and take thine which is but of cheese?' The Serb chats with him: 'How much money dost thou want?' When the Gypsy heard about money he was willing to strike a bargain. I do not know how much gold he got from the Serb for that church, but it appears that the Serbian was short by thirty paras! Thus the Gypsy passed into the church of cheese.

When the Gypsies entered this church of cheese one of them stood up and took a lump of cheese. But when the other Gypsies saw what he had done they wanted to kill him. 'Stop, brothers,' he exclaimed, 'why use such force? I only took a morsel to see how this cheese tasted.' And he broke off a lump of cheese and gave them each a piece. When the Gypsies found how good the cheese tasted, they began to break off pieces; and before you had time to strike one palm against the other the church had disappeared. They ate it all.

When the Gypsies had eaten their church they had nowhere to pray to God. They went to the Serbs: 'Listen, you, will you pay us the remainder of the money which you were not able to give us?' But the Serbs had no more money. They think over what they should do. 'Listen, Gypsies, we have no money to hand over to you. Let us make a bargain. We will admit you into our church to pray until we can turn over to you the remainder of your money.'

But to this very day the Serbs have not been able to hand over to the Gypsies their money. That is why the Gypsy goes to the Serbian church. And that is why Gypsy women to this very day go begging with a bag from house to house.

HUNGARIAN

Recorded by Vladislav Kornel

---

21. The Creation of the World

When there was nothing on earth and in the universe but an immense quantity of water, God determined to create the world, but he did not know how to go about it. Annoyed at his awkwardness, the more so as he had neither a brother nor a friend who could give him good advice, he threw into the water a stick on which he was leaning, while promenading the clouds. When the stick fell into the water, a gigantic tree grew immediately out of it, the roots of which settled in the deep. On one of the branches of this tree sat the Devil, who was then still white, like mankind afterwards created by God.

'Dear little God! dear brother mine!' cried the Devil, smiling, 'I am sorry for thee, indeed! thou hast neither brother nor friend. Well, then, I will be thy brother and friend.'

'Oh, nothing of the sort!' replied God, 'a brother thou canst not be to me; nobody can be my brother. But be my friend!'

Nine days after this conversation, when the Lord had not yet created the world, as he did not know how to proceed, he perceived during one of his walks that the Devil was not friendly towards him. The Devil, who was not stupid, observed that God distrusted him, and he therefore said to him: 'Dear brother mine, art thou aware that we two do not suit each other? Have therefore the kindness to create one more, so that there may be three of us.'

'Faith! it is easy to say create another,' replied God, very sorrowfully, 'create thou him if thou art so wise!'

'But I am not able to do it', cried the Devil. 'I would have long ere this created a beautiful large world, but of what use is my wish, when I do not know how to go about it, my dear brother?'

'Well,' said God thoughtfully, scratching his head, as if trying to remember something, 'I shall create the world, and thou art to assist me. Quick, then, without loss of time, dive under the water and bring out of the deep a handful of sand, to form out of it the earth.'

'Indeed?' said the Devil, seemingly surprised; 'and how shalt thou do this? It is incomprehensible to me!'

'I shall utter my name, and the sand will shape itself into the globe', replied God; 'but now, quick, bring the sand!'

The Devil dived under, saying to himself, 'Oh, I am not so stupid that I should allow the creation of the world to be done by another. I shall do it myself, by calling out my name.'

When the Devil arrived at the bottom of the deep, he took hold of the sand with both hands, but when he called out his name he was obliged to drop the sand, as it burned his hands.

When the Devil returned he told God that he could not find any sand. 'Go, seek it, but bring what I have commanded.' For nine days the Devil insisted that he could find no sand, which was a lie, as he tried continually to create the world out of the sand of the deep, but as often as he took the sand in his hands and called out his name he burned himself; the sand grew hotter and burned him so terribly that one day it came about that he turned black as coal.

When God perceived the Devil, he said to him: 'Thou hast turned black, I see, and hast been a bad friend. Hurry now, bring sand out of the deep, but do not utter thy name, or the sea will consume thee.'

The Devil dived under and carried out the command given to him. God took the sand, called his name, and the world was made, which greatly pleased the Devil.

'Here', said he, sitting down in the shade of a large tree, 'under this tree shall I dwell, and thou, dear brother, canst look out for other quarters.' This impudence angered the Lord so much that he called out: 'Ah! you rogue, only wait —I will teach you sense; be off at once!'

At that moment an immense ox rushed out of the copse, took the Devil on his horns, and ran with him into the wide world. Fear and pain made the Devil shriek so loud that the leaves fell from the trees and changed into men.

Thus did the Lord create the world and the people therein, with the assistance of the Devil.

22. The Hungarian, the German, the Jew, and the Gypsy

When the great Mara (God the Father) created the world, he also created man, and among others a Hungarian, a German, a Jew, and a Gypsy.

The Hungarian was born in a magnificent castle, where he immediately sat down to table, on which *gulas* and other fine dishes and cans of golden wine were standing. The Hungarian ate and drank, and was quite at his ease.

The German was born in a light cart, drawn by a large dog. The dog with the cart and the new-born baby stopped before an inn. After stretching himself a little the German sat down to table, drinking mug after mug of beer. He considered how he could oust the Hungarian from the castle, and get possession of it.

The Jew was born under the counter of the taproom in which the German drank his beer. The Jew immediately took a piece of chalk and jotted down (twice over) the number of glasses of beer consumed by the German, as well as the glasses of wine drunk by the Hungarian, and then he made his reckoning, and the German and the Hungarian paid him in hard cash, which he put into his pocket, satisfying his hunger with a head of a herring and a piece of garlic.

The Gypsy was born on the grassy *pushta*, in the shade of a single tree, that grew there. The light zephyr kissed his forehead, the rain washed and baptized him, and the stork sitting on his nest was his godfather. No one took care of the Gypsy. When he rose from the grass he perceived a fiddle hanging on the tree; he seized it, and played such a *csardas* that the stork rattled his beak for joy. He went into the inn playing without ceasing.

The German drank the beer, and with the nets which he took out of his little cart he surrounded with snares the Hungarian who was sitting in his castle. The Jew sang the 'Majufes', counting into his money-bag the dollars which fell out of the pockets of the German and the Hungarian. The Hungarian did not mind anything; he ate and drank unconcernedly.

When the Hungarian, the German, and the Jew heard the music of the Gypsy, they listened attentively, smiled joyously, and at last commenced to dance. The Hungarian skipped about like one possessed, twirled round like a peg, cowered on the ground twisting his moustaches, and clashing his spurs. The German, who was as full of beer as a cask, turned slowly and awkwardly round, without forgetting, however, to ensnare the Hungarian with his nets, as a spider does a fly. The Jew skipped about lightly, putting in his bag the dollars that rolled about the floor.

When the Gypsy, being tired, ceased playing, the Hungarian gave him a can of wine, the German a half-emptied mug of beer, and the Jew half a silver dollar, biting off a piece with his teeth. The Hungarian continued drinking wine and dancing like mad; the German assuaged his thirst with beer and hopped about; and the Jew nodded his head singing 'bim! bim' and counting his dollars.

To this day the Hungarian dances and drinks wine; the German drinks beer and skips about, trying at any price to ensnare the Hungarian; and the Jew counts his dollars and laughs at the Hungarian and the German. And the Gypsy? He plays his *csardas*, drinks wine or beer, and occasionally gets chipped dollars from the Jew.

23. How a Gypsy Cheated the Devil

Once, when the Gypsy went into the *Csarda* (an inn in the *pushta*) he played on his fiddle such a sad, plaintive, and melancholy tune that the blades of grass and the bulrushes were covered with tears, with dew. 'Twas thus he sang:

As a prisoner I am guarded;
At my right hand stalks my shadow
And my thoughts drag close behind me,
Like some harsh and cruel warder!

pondering the while why he was condemned to poverty, scorn, loathing and unceasing travel. The strains of the sweet but sad melody sounded far and near, carried on the wings of the playful zephyr, losing themselves among the bulrushes, and making an echo that seemed to pity the Gypsy's lot.

The Devil, who lived in an old willow on the banks of a bog, heard this lament, and, seized with compassion for the Gypsy, resolved to help him. As the Gypsy pursued his way, playing and singing, he saw a Suabian leap out of the dry grass, clothed in a short frockcoat, a pipe in his mouth, and a velvet cap on his head. The Gypsy, astonished to see a stranger so far from the *Csarda*, stopped.

'Eh! what is the matter?' said the Devil, surveying him from head to foot; 'have I frightened you, that you cease playing and singing?' 'Ah! why should I be frightened, Mr German?' replied the Gypsy, smiling cunningly as he perceived on his head two horns, which the cap did not cover entirely. 'Very well, but if I were the Devil would you be afraid of me?' 'Oh', replied the Gypsy, scratching his head, 'is the Devil more terrible than a German? To tell the truth, just now I would prefer to meet the Devil, as he might help me in my misfortune and my need!'

'Excellent,' replied the Devil, 'if this is the case, speak. I am he whom you want; I will help you!' 'Indeed!' said the Gypsy; 'for what purpose have you assumed this garb? If you are really the Devil, you must be aware that every Gypsy and every Hungarian would rather have intercourse with a devil than with a German. Besides it is a matter of indifference to me whether you are a devil or a Suabian— only help me.'

'All right,' replied the Devil, 'but you must give me what is dearest to you!' 'Yes; but what do I possess that is dearest to me, unless it is this fiddle?' 'That is it,' answered the Devil, 'you will give me your fiddle!' 'But what shall I do without it?' 'You shall be rich; I will give you heaps of gold.' 'Ahem!'

said the Gypsy, deep in thought. After a while he replied, smiling to himself, 'And what will you, Mr Devil, do with the fiddle?' 'I shall play on it, and everybody will follow me wherever I wish.' 'Very well, then, but first carry out your promise!' 'With pleasure; but remember that your fiddle belongs to me, otherwise you will fare badly! Now, bestride this bulrush, as if it were a horse, and follow me.'

The Gypsy obeyed the bidding of the Devil, and in one moment both flew through the air towards the East. The sun was about setting, when the Devil and the Gypsy alighted from their airy steeds, by the Szamos-between-the-Mountains. The Devil took hold of the Gypsy's hand, leading him to a waterfall, and took out of the shallow bed of the river a handful of gravel, giving it to the Gypsy.

'Here is what I promised. The bottom of this river and the cave behind the waterfall are covered with gold. It is all yours; but give me your fiddle.' The Gypsy stared astonished at the gravel, which glittered like gold. After a while, as if distrusting what he saw, he went and picked up some gravel and sand; they were pure gold. 'Indeed you have kept your word', said the Gypsy; 'it is now my turn; only permit me to take leave of my fiddle.' And so wonderfully did the Gypsy play, that not only the Devil, but heaven also wept.

The Gypsy kissed the fiddle at the last plaintive note, placed his lips to one of the openings, sucked the air out of it, and handed it to the Devil, who disappeared with it like mist. The Gypsy filled his pipe, lighted it, and commenced taking gold out of the bed of the Szamos.

After the lapse of three days the Gypsy was very rich, but his longing for his fiddle was still greater. Tired and heartsore, he sat down on one of the heaps of gold, saying, 'Devil, thou art clever but I am not stupid; I gave thee my fiddle, but not my soul which plays on its strings.'

Then suddenly the Devil appeared, and returning the fiddle to the Gypsy, he said, 'I have made a bad bargain; thou hast the gold, but instead of alluring men with the sound of thy fiddle, I have frightened them away. Take back therefore thy fiddle, for though I am a devil, I cannot play like thee. But, before parting, how comes it that, when thou playest, the fiddle sings so wonderfully?'

'Well,' replied the Gypsy, taking the instrument out of the devil's hand, 'it is but natural. I gave thee the fiddle as promised, but kept the soul for myself!' And the Gypsy placed his lips to one of the openings of the fiddle, breathed into it, and played such a passionate *csardas*, that the Devil skipped about like one possessed, and the Gypsy himself was greatly astonished at his own playing—he thought he had never played like this before.

'Ah! I see now;' said the Devil, when the Gypsy had finished playing, 'I was a great fool to let myself be cheated by a Gypsy. Thou gavest me the fiddle, but without thy soul. Well, it is done, and cannot be helped; thou hast my gold and the fiddle, but thy playing will allure men into my net!'

From that time onwards the devils in hell no longer dance the waltz but the *csardas*. And the Gypsy receives money for the *csardas*, which he alone can play so wonderfully. And the Devil, though he had been cheated by the Gypsy, lost nothing by it, as men are still falling into his net the same as before.

RUMANIAN

Recorded by Dr Moses Gaster

─────────────────

24. The Golden Children

There was once an Emperor's son: this prince, what was he to do? He went to his father, and said: 'Father, it behoves me to marry, does it not, father?' 'My son, if thou desirest to marry, I too desire it: find thyself a wife.' 'I will certainly find one.'

He departed and went on foot and on horseback: but he did not find a wife. Returning home to his father, to one of his palaces, he passed in front of the Emperor's courtyard. Three maidens were sitting outside in the porch. And the eldest sister said: 'Peter, Peter, beautiful youth, take even me, for I have a crust of bread with which I can nourish all the armies thou or thy father may'st have, however numerous they be.'

And the midmost sister said: 'Take even me, for I can maintain thy whole army, for with this single thread of yarn thou couldst make all their uniforms.'

And the youngest said: 'Do thou take me, Peter, for I will bear thee two golden children, with silver teeth and golden hair, and two apples in their hands all golden.' 'I will choose thee', said he to the youngest. He took her and went home.

He made a wedding feast, and brought fiddlers, and they sat down, and they ate and drank and ate and drank. And they danced for three days and nights. Night fell, and still they ate and drank. In the morning the pair arose and went to the priest. They were married and came home.

A year passed after Peter took her to wife: she became with child. The two sisters in their rage against her, what did they do? They went to the village midwife and said: 'Midwife, we kiss thy hands and thy feet; if thou wilt do us a favour, we will give thee a bushel of ducats. Do thou go to our sister when the time comes for her to be delivered, and substitute two puppies for the babes, and take the children, and do to her what thou thinkest best.' She set out for their sister's home.

And the Emperor's son, what did he say? 'Here, midwife! I will give thee a bushel of ducats: if only thou savest the head of my wife, then I will give thee a bushel of ducats.' 'So be it! Emperor, I will do so. But the birth must not be in the house, it must be in the loft.'

She took the lady and put her in the loft. The lady gave birth to two children. As beautiful as is the sun, so beautiful were they. Their bones could be seen through their skin, and the marrow through the bones, so beautiful were they.

She took them and threw them to the pigs for a pig to devour. But one pig among them said: 'O pigs, do not devour them, for these babes will become our masters who will give us food to eat.' So he took them and laid them near a brood sow, and they sucked until daybreak.

The midwife, seeing that the pigs had not devoured the children, threw them to the horses for a horse to eat. And one horse among them said: 'O horses, do not devour them, for these babes will become our masters.' This horse took them, and laid them near a mare, and they sucked until daybreak.

The village midwife, seeing that the horses had not devoured them, threw them to the oxen. A bull was about to toss them on its horns, when one ox among them said: 'O oxen, do not devour them, for these babes will become our masters.' He took them and laid them near a cow: they sucked until daybreak.

The midwife, seeing that the oxen did not devour the children, took them and threw them into the river. God, seeing this, would not allow them to drown, but brought them to the bank.

An old man saw them there. He said: 'These are now my children.' What was the Emperor's son to do? The fisherman brought them up until they grew big and had reached their seventh year. The boy and girl crossed to the other side of the river and built themselves a house over there.

The midwife, seeing that they were not dead, came to the

bank of the river, and called across to the girl: 'Girl, girl, tell thy brother to go and bring thee the crown of the Snake—he will be nine years going from the tail to the head, to get this Snake's crown.' 'Flee from here', she answered, 'or I will arouse my brother, he will order his horse to kick thee, his white horse.'

The village midwife fled. The girl, his cunning sister, lay down to sleep; when she arose she said that she had had a dream. 'Brother, I dreamed that thou must journey for nine years, and yet another nine (and they make eighteen!), from the tail to the head of the Snake.'

He saddled his horse, and rode on farther, and still farther, as far as the Snake's tail. He went farther still till he came to Luya. 'Good morning, little Mother Monday.' 'And what dost thou seek? Why hast thou come hither?' 'I have not come looking sleek and fair; I have come in great sorrow. My sister dreamed that I should bring her the Snake's crown.' 'Go with God, and with long days!'

He went, and he reached the Snake's head. Before it were lying heaps of bones, bones of men that had been eaten by the Snake. But how could he manage to seize the crown of the Snake? He let his horse run straight ahead, and then doubled back towards the crown, stretched out his hand and snatched it, the Snake's crown. He gave rein to his horse, and fled straight to the house of Monday, with the Snake at his heels, trying to catch up to him that it might devour him.

And he said to Monday: 'Oh! Mother Monday, do not let the unclean Snake devour me—look! here he comes towards us.' Monday went outside: 'O unclean Snake, wherefore comest thou in this fashion to my house?' 'A man who fled here and is hidden in thy house brought me.' 'He is not here!' 'Sister, sister, put him outside, that I may see what manner of man he is; may God strike me dead if I devour him!' Monday put him outside. The Snake saw that he was a beautiful youth. 'O brother, what beautiful bones thou hast for gnawing! go thy way, brother, go with God.' 'Remain with God.'

He came home to his sister. 'Here, sister, I have brought thee what thou didst demand.' 'Brother, mayst thou be blessed of God for bringing me what I asked, the crown of the Snake. Brother, what we now have, not even the Emperor has.'

When the village midwife heard that the boy had not been killed, she donned her clothes, drew on her shoes, crossed herself, and came there in hot haste. She came to a spot opposite to where his house stood. If she crossed over the river, she feared she would die. So she went on, and left the river behind. The village midwife looked all around, and listened. What did she say? 'Girl, girl, let thy brother fetch Ileana Simziana, and take her to wife.' 'Flee from here', answered the girl, 'for I am enraged, and if I arouse my brother, he will kick thee, and give thee such a blow on the neck, that thou wilt spew naught but blood.' The village midwife heard and fled.

The girl lay down to sleep: she crossed herself and arose as if from slumber. 'Brother, I dreamed that thou must go and take Ileana Simziana for wife. Brother, not even the Emperor has what we have.'

The brother saddled his horse, crossed himself, and went to God, close to the threshold of heaven, until he reached the Pear-tree of Ileana. The pears were full of worms. The Snake had bidden him eat one of the worm-eaten pears, and say: 'My God, my God, since my mother bore me, never have I eaten such a beautiful pear, nor one so sweet as this.' And the Pear-tree, what did she say? 'Brother, brother, of the many who have passed here, all have spat upon me, but thou alone didst me a kindness: I will repay it.'

He went on farther and reached a Blackthorn: the sloes were full of worms. What did he say? 'God! how sweet are these sloes which I pluck for eating.' He plucked, eats them, and said: 'God, God, since my mother bore me, never have I tasted sloes so sweet.' And the Blackthorn: 'So many have passed here,' she said, and all had spat upon her, the Blackthorn; and when in her wrath Ileana so commanded, she would catch every one of them. And Peter the handsome went on eating the sloes, and said: 'Sloes so sweet I never ate since my mother bore me.' And the Blackthorn said: 'Go with God, brother.' 'Remain with God.'

He went on farther, and came to a Spring. He sat down and drew water and drank. He said: 'My God, my God, since my mother bore me, never have I drunk such good water.'

At last he came to the palace of Ileana. He did not go through the sunlight, because she had twelve bulls there; he crawled on his belly through the shade for then the bulls would not notice him. And so he came into the palace, and seized her by the hair, and well-nigh beat her to death like a dog. She said: 'Peter, Peter, thou beautiful one, loose my hair, and I will marry thee.' He loosed her hair, lifted her on to his horse, rode away, and came to the Spring.

And what said Ileana? 'Oh, Spring, seize him!' And the Spring, what did she say? 'I hear, mistress; but I will not seize him, because so many passed here and spat upon me, and he alone in passing drank my water, and said to God: "My God, my God! such water have I never drunk since my mother bore me." '

He rode on, and came to the River. 'River, River, seize him!' 'I will not seize him, mistress, because so many passed here and spat upon me, and he alone in passing drank my water, and said to God: "Never once before have I tasted such water." '

He rode on, and came to the Blackthorn. 'Seize him!' 'I will not seize him, mistress, because so many passed this way and spat upon me, and he alone in passing plucked sloes from me and began to eat, and said to God: "My God, my God, such sweet sloes I have never tasted since my mother bore me." '

He went on farther, and came to the Pear-tree. And what said Ileana Simziana? 'Pear-tree, seize him!' 'I will not seize him, for all who passed here spat upon me, and he in passing praised me.'

Ileana, seeing that she had no longer any power, returned home. She took him for her husband, and was married by the priest. Afterwards they went home to his sister.

When the village midwife heard of it, she came to the opposite bank, and called out to the girl: 'Girl, girl, send thy brother to bring thee the Tree that sings and the Bird that talks, for wondrous beautiful as ye are now, ye will become more beautiful still.' 'Flee from here', she answered, 'for if I arouse my brother, he will order his horse to kick thee.' In fear the midwife fled back to her house.

The girl, what was she to do? She lay down to sleep. She pretended to arise as if from sleep, and said: 'Brother, brother, do thou go and bring me the Talking Bird and the Singing Tree.'

For very shame he could not refuse her, so he saddled his horse, and set out for the river and the forest: he reached the spot. He rode farther and farther and still farther, until he came to the Tree.

As soon as the Bird espied him, it called out: 'Whither art thou going, poor man?' He did not answer, while he was climbing the Tree. 'Whither art thou going, poor man?' the Bird asked again. 'To thee.' Down he fell, and was turned into a stone.

And Ileana Simziana sensed that he was dead. She dressed herself as a man, and set out after him, until she reached her husband. And the Bird espied her, and perceived that she was a woman. 'Whither goest thou, poor woman?' She did not answer, until she had climbed the twelve boughs and laid her hand upon the Bird. From it she plucked one feather, and then let it go. She climbed down again, went up to the stone, struck it with the feather, and made her husband arise. She left the plum-tree there, and came home.

The next morning after she had returned, lo! there stood the Tree and the Bird in front of the house. The Bird began to talk and the Tree to sing. And the village midwife could find naught else to do to them. The boy celebrated his wedding.

One day the Emperor's son, their father, riding along came to the bank of the river, when he saw on the other side the beautiful palace and the Singing Tree in front of it. When the Bird beheld him it said: 'Welcome, Emperor, whom art thou seeking?' The Emperor's son, greatly astonished, asked the Bird who was living in that palace. 'Who else but your own children, whom your jealous sisters-in-law wanted to destroy? They bribed the midwife to place a puppy dog and a puppy bitch under your wife, and the children she cast into the river. They are living here.'

The Emperor's son, when he heard these words did not know how to cross the river quickly enough to satisfy himself of the truth of the Bird's speech. For ever since he had returned from the war and the midwife had told him of the puppies to which his wife had given birth instead of the two promised golden children, he had put his wife into a dungeon behind the palace with the two pups to suckle. When he entered the house he found the girl with a crown upon her head more glorious than his, and the boy with his fairy wife Ileana Simziana. His children were of gold with silver teeth and golden hair, as their mother had promised. He recognized them at once, and taking them with him he returned quickly to the palace. Thither they brought his wife, who on seeing the children became young and beautiful again. The Emperor's son ordered the midwife to be torn to pieces by wild horses, and the two sisters, who had been living in the palace all the time, he ordered to be banished from the country. And henceforth they all lived happily together.

25. The Iron Man

There was a King. He had three sons, and the time came when they grew up. Lo! they went and said to their father: 'Father, we wish to marry.' And their father said to them: 'My boys, do ye take your spears and fling them up towards God: where your spears fall, thence shall ye bring your wives.'

The spear of the eldest brother fell to the Red Emperor. And that of the middle brother fell to the Red King. And they had to take his daughters to themselves as wives. But the spear of his youngest son fell into a swamp.

So these three boys arose and came to their father. And their father asked them: 'What have ye done, my sons?'

So the eldest arose and said to his father: 'My spear fell to the Red Emperor, and I will take his daughter to wife.' His father said: 'Thou art good, my boy.'

And the middle brother said: 'My spear fell to the Red King.' And his father said: 'Thou art good, my boy.'

And the youngest brother said to his father: 'Father, my spear fell into a swamp.' His father said that he must flee from him: 'For thou art an unlucky man. My two elder sons are luckier. And I will make a great wedding-feast, and I shall parade myself, eating and drinking at my son's wedding.' And he set to, and made a wedding-feast—just as we, the Gypsies, do. And he danced at the wedding until the feast was broken up.

Then this son went off to collect for himself and stow away the property of his young bride which her father had promised her, and afterwards they returned to his father's house.

So when the bride's father-in-law came outside, he began to laugh at the fine sight before him, for he saw his son with the young woman looking like a wealthy lord. So this grand father-in-law told the servants to collect the possessions which his son's rich wife had brought.

Then he spoke to his youngest son and said: 'Get thee away into the world somewhere, that I may no longer see thee as a penniless man.'

So the youngest son took his spear and set off for the swamp. When he reached the swamp he says to himself: 'Here lies my fortune.' The boy set to, to build himself a hut where he might lodge: and he soon made the hut ready for use. Then he thought that he must buckle to and get some food. So he seized his gun to go hunting for birds and ravens and wolves.

The boy set off and caught some game, picked it up, and came back to his hut. And he is hungry when he looks into his hut. And he saw the table spread, so he started to eat. Then he rose from the table and crossed himself, saying: 'Who has done me this kindness? If I could but see him I would give him everything he demanded.'

The boy set off again, and walked from early morn until nightfall. And he caught nothing but a quail: not a thing more. The boy came back to his hut.

There arose a silver girl from out the swamp, and she stepped out of her covering of reeds and became a human being. She set to and washed the dishes and prepared victuals, neither too hot nor too cold but exactly right for the boy to eat.

The girl hid herself. The boy tried to catch her, and he laid his hand upon her, and kissed her and said that she should become his wife.

She said: 'It will be a bad thing, my boy, because I should have had a little longer until the proper time came for me to be thy wife.' But he took her to wife. He goes, and fetched his game. And she prepares it and eats and drinks with her husband like everybody else.

And his wife arose and goes and calls her Iron Brother, and said to him: 'My brother, build for me a house within a certain time, and that is by the time my husband returns from where he has gone. For I want to live with my husband.'

Much time passes. Then her husband says: 'Let us go to my father, wife.' The wife answered: 'It will be evil for thee, husband, it will not turn out well. But since thou sayest: "Let us go", come! let levies be imposed on everyone, that ye do not go home empty-handed.'

Now they went home, to his father. And when the King saw that his son's wife was silvern, and such a wondrous being that she had not an equal, the father straightway said to his son that if he did not feed his whole army on a single cabbage he would cut his throat and take his wife.

He came weeping to his wife. The wife said to him: 'Did I not tell thee not to return to thy father, for all would not be well? Seek thy brother-in-law and call him. Say to him: "Iron Man, do for me what I request." ' 'What dost thou request?' asked the Iron Man. 'My father demands that I feed his whole army on a single cabbage.'

Then his brother-in-law, the Iron Man, told him to go and bring twenty-four young buffaloes 'that we may go and drag it out, for it is a cabbage which for twenty-four years has been fed on water.'

The young boy hurried to his father and asks him for twenty-four buffaloes to bring the cabbage to him. As soon as the father heard, he gave him the buffaloes.

The youngest son set off and arrived at his brother-in-law's. His brother-in-law saw that he had brought the beasts. They fastened chains to the cabbage and he roused the buffaloes; they struck them with their clubs. Thus was the cabbage uprooted.

And he brought it to his father. His father looked at it. He said: 'My son, do thou go home and rest.' When they cut into the cabbage they had not eaten half of the half and they were satisfied. What can the King do to kill his son so that he may take his wife?

The King had him fetched and told him that he must bring him the ring which he had exchanged with the Queen on their wedding-day, and her handkerchief as well. The boy asked: 'Then where is thy Queen?' The King replied: 'She has been dead now eighteen years.' 'Where is the ring?' 'On her finger.' The boy said: 'How shall I bring it if my mother is dead? What if I don't bring it?' The father said to him: 'Lo! there is a knife! and there is thy neck! if thou dost not bring it thou wilt be slain and thy wife will become mine.'

He set off, and says to his wife's brother: 'My father desires to kill me.' He, the wife's brother, questioned him. 'Be not afraid!' says the wife's brother, 'what he demands I, the Iron Man, will do.'

The Iron Man sent his brother-in-law to his father to beg for two spurred cocks. And he comes back and brought the cocks, and they mounted them and left for the Other World.

They depart, and they came to a cow in a meadow by the waters, on an island fed by springs. And there was not enough flesh upon her to put on the point of a needle. And he asked the Iron Man: 'Why is not this cow fat?' He answered him: 'When we come back, I will tell thee.'

And they came to a cow upon the sand: if thou wert to lay thy finger upon her she would burst with fat. He said to his brother-in-law, the Iron Man: 'This cow is fed upon the sand, and see! she seems well nourished; that other was fed on abundance, and yet she is lean!' The Iron Man answered him: 'Let it be! when we come back I will explain, when we turn round.'

And they went on. They came to the Dead and they are dancing—his mother with the handkerchief in her hand, and the ring on her finger. The Iron Man said to his brother-in-law: 'Now in yonder place thou must go secretly up to thy mother, and put thy hand out to seize the handkerchief and draw off the ring, and do not make a sound lest thou remain for ever with the Dead in yonder land. I would go thither myself but I have quarrelled with the archangel. As soon as thou approachest thy mother she will call out, but do not desire her to give thee the ring; she will wail over thee, but do not fear, for I, even I, am here, the Iron Man: there is nothing they can do to thee in my presence.'

And they went to his mother: and he found himself among the Dead, who were eating and drinking and singing. His mother called to him: 'Come hither, son!' He put out his hand and drew off the ring, and returned to his brother-in-law, the Iron Man.

And they turned round after they had done what they wanted. He and his brother-in-law reached the lean cow. He asked his brother-in-law, the Iron Man: 'Why does not the cow grow fat?' The Iron Man answered: 'If the parent did not provide for his child with his whole heart when he baptized it, things would not prosper with him.' They set off and reached the fat cow, and see how it thrives upon the sand! Its mother and father have provided for it with their whole heart, so that it may be blessed by a numerous offspring; yea, the parent gave his whole heart to cause his child to prosper.

Then he returned to the upper world. He set forth, and they came to his father, the King. He rose very early and washed himself and made the sign of the cross. He went to his father. The father also was up betimes and was in his dressing-gown. 'Good morning to thee, father.' The father looked at him askance. And the father said to him: 'Wicked one, why hast thou come?' The son answered: 'There is what thou didst ask of me: what thou didst demand, I have brought thee.' He gave the ring to him, to his father. 'And take the handkerchief, for what thou didst demand I have done.' The father said: 'There is one more thing thou must do for me: for if thou dost not bring me an Iron Man I will cut thee into little bits, and give thee to the snakes to lick thy bones.'

The boy went off weeping to his wife. And the wife asked her husband: 'Why dost thou weep?' 'My father said that if I do not bring him an Iron Man, then he will cut me into little bits, and throw me to his snakes, that they may lick my bones.' His wife said: 'Come no more weeping to me, for what thou demandest, I will perform like a strong woman, as I have the power to do. Go thou, call thy brother-in-law, say to him: "My father summons thee."' The Iron Man said: 'God smite him! because in spite of what I have done for him he would not let me rest this day.'

The Iron Man took his iron chair and put it in his pocket, and he took his ladder and set forth.

And he came to the King. But wherever he places his foot the wooden stairs break, until at last there was no longer any spot for him to stand. And the King is afraid that what he has done has not been done well.

So the Iron Man set down his iron ladder and climbed up the staircase. And he said to the King: 'Why didst thou summon me?' 'I summoned thee to eat with me at table.'

He started to put one chair after another under him. But whatever he puts under him breaks, until it came about that he had to seek for something else to sit upon. Then he pulled out his iron chair from his pocket and asked the King: 'Why didst thou summon me to eat with thee? God grant that when next thou eatest with me at table, thou mayest still be a live man!' And then he gave him a blow with his iron hand which struck him dead on the spot.

He left him there dead, and returned to his sister and his brother-in-law. And he, his brother-in-law, asked: 'What hast thou done?' He said that he had killed the King.

They set to, and appointed a man to prepare a banquet for them. And the Iron Man sent to fetch musicians for them. And then they all ate and drank and made much noise. He prepared a wedding-feast that lasted for three days and three nights. Then his wife showed him that her silver hair had become golden.

Then the Iron Man said: 'Hereafter in my presence no one will be able to do any harm to anyone, neither in this world nor yet in the other shall anyone harm anyone else.'

26. The Wife from the Other World

There were three brothers. Of these three brothers two were very rich and one was very poor. Now what said the poor one to his wife? 'Go, get for us three measures of corn from thy brothers, that we may put it in the cauldron to cook.' She brought the corn from her brothers.

And what did she say to him? 'Oh, husband, it is not right

to cook it; it would be better to go and beg thy brothers to
help for three days to cut ten furrows for thee, so that we may
sow the corn for a crop. When the time comes and it is full-
grown, we will reap the corn, and it will presently bring us
all sorts of benefits.'

And when his brothers reaped the corn the field was black.
When the poor brother saw that his corn had not grown, he
gave it to the devil. Then the devil, what did he do? In one
night he made it grow. The next morning when the man
came to his corn, he found it, let us say, stack-high, and better
and even higher. The ears were of gold and the stalks of
silver. Then what did he do? He made ready to reap it.

And the Devil, what will he do to the man? He gave him a
slap in the face. 'And thou, what dost thou here?' 'I am reap-
ing my corn.' 'And how comes it thine?' 'I tilled it.' 'Even if
thou didst till it, thou didst present it to the Devil.' 'Art thou
the Devil?' 'I am.' 'And wilt thou not give me back my
corn?' 'No, I won't.'

The man returned and went to his wife. 'Quick, wife, make
me a cake of bread, for the Devil has set himself up as master
of our corn.' 'Let him, husband, for I will outwit him.' . . .

She won the contest with the Devil, outwitted him, and
went home to her husband. 'Ho! wife.' 'My husband, the
corn remains ours.'

'Oh, wife, make a little cake and send our son to keep watch
over the corn, (for the ears are of gold and the stalks of silver)
lest a raven come and snatch an ear, and there be murder
and ruin.' But the raven came, plucked an ear in its beak,
and the boy ran after it to catch it. He reached an untrodden
forest.

Then the boy, what can he do? He began to weep. He
started to walk along a little path, and he came to a huge
giant. He found him by the fire; nine cart-loads of wood were
thrown on to that fire. The giant stretched out in three directions, three times the length of the fire.

And what can the boy do? He lay down behind the giant
to sleep. When the giant awoke, he leapt up from his sleep—
and his leap was as far as nine years' journey of an ordinary
person—because he sensed that there was a human being
near him: and his fears smote him again when he actually

saw the boy asleep behind him. And the boy arose. He began to cry with his head in his hands. The giant saw that he was weeping. He said: 'I will make him my son; I will take this lad thrice to my bosom and my heart.'

When the boy perceived this he said: 'Oh, father, I will go off to the forest to see what I can bring you: wild fowl, hares, wolves. And now, do thou keep the house warm, so that when I return I may find it warm, well-warmed, this house of mine beneath the pines. Do thou go for water, and fetch both water and wood, so that I may feel that I too have a father.'

The boy went on his way. He found three drops of blood, the face of the earth white as snow, and a feather of a raven. And what said the boy? 'Why can I not have a wife as beautiful as those tokens I have found: red as blood, white as snow, and black as a raven? What thinkest thou, father?' 'If, my son, thou shouldst desire me to get thee married, I will blow my horn for three days and three nights, so that three maidens may come from the other world to dance in the road. And do thou draw near to the middlemost sister, and dance three times with her, and put out thy hand, snatch the crown from her and flee back quickly to me. Thou must not turn round, or she will snatch it out of thy hand and thou wilt be left without her.' And he asked: 'What do they call the country from which the three sisters come?' 'Let us say: "The Other World."'

So the boy replies: 'Father, what sayest thou if I set forth after them?' 'Let me blow my horn for three days and three nights, so that the three sisters may come and begin to dance in the road. And do thou join the dance with the middlemost sister.'

So he blew his horn for three days and three nights. Lo and behold! the girls appeared and danced in the road. From the middlemost sister he seized the crown in his hand and began to flee. So she called after him: 'Oh, my Peter, give me back my crown.' He turned round and she snatched the treasure out of his hand. She flew off at once, and the other two flew away also.

And the giant went on blowing. Three maidens appeared on the spot, and alighted on the road and danced there. And the boy came and joined them and took three turns. And with his hand he seized this crown surreptitiously, and placed it in his bosom. And the eldest sister cried out after him: 'Here, Peter, look behind, how beautiful I am, with my face as white as snow and red as three drops of blood, and hair as black as a raven's feather.' Then he turned round. So she flew away.

To his little father he said: 'Oh, my father!' 'What hast thou done, boy?' 'She has outwitted me.' 'I must set to and blow my horn once more.' So the giant set to and blew his horn for three days and three nights.

Lo and behold! after three days the three sisters appeared. Peter drew near to the youngest sister on the road and they danced. He joined them in the dance three times. Then he laid his hand on the head of the youngest sister and seized her crown. He started to run away. And the youngest sister, what said she? 'Oh, my Peter, look back at me and see how beautiful I am, and that my face is as white as snow.' So he looked; and she snatched the crown from his hand suddenly and flew away with great ease.

To his father, what did he say? 'Oh, little father!' 'What hast thou done, boy? Thou didst not do well to let her outwit thee thus. But once more I will blow my horn for three days and three nights, that the three sisters may appear again. Do thou draw near to the eldest sister and take a turn in the dance on the road, and set thy hand on her, the eldest sister, and snatch the crown from this one's head, and place it in thy bosom, and give it to me to hide so that she may become thy wife. Then she will come by herself and thou shalt take her to wife, to make a home and have children like the rest of the world, if thou knowest how to attract her to thy house by night.' Lo and behold! the eldest sister came and he took her to wife.

Then he raised his hand and began to scratch his head; he began to weep. His foster father said: 'Oh, my boy, what art thou crying for? Has she brought to thy mind thine own father and mother? Wouldst thou like me to make thee a carriage as swift as the wind or as swift as death?' 'Oh, father, make me one like the wind.' So he made it as swift as the wind. The boy took his seat in the carriage with his wife. 'Oh, father, give me the crown as well.' 'See that she does not out-wit thee and leave thee on the road.' 'She will not outwit me.' The giant handed over the crown.

So he set forth and came to his real father. 'Oh, father, how dost thou?' 'Quite well: and thou, how dost thou?' When they looked into one another's eyes, they began to kiss and to weep. 'Oh, my father, what wilt thou do?' 'I will make a wedding-feast for thy young sister's bridegroom.'

He proceeded to make the wedding-feast. And they brought the feast to an end. And his son started dancing with a strange woman. 'If this old man's wife', he said, 'can dance as well as mine, I will offer 500 ducats and 200 paras.' And so the two women began to dance. The old man's wife dances with her feet just touching the ground, but the young man's wife dances in the air with her feet far above the ground, and Peter's wife far surpassed the old man's wife.

'Oh, father and mother, tell Peter to give me my crown that I may put it on my head, for then I can spring ten times higher than now.' His father said: 'Give it to her.' 'No, father, I won't give it, for she would leave me here and she is with child.' But she urged him with all her desire until he gave it up. She danced for a little, and then said to her husband: 'Good-bye, fare thee well, for I am going away.'

So he became frightened and closed the doors. He did not know that she would burst asunder the roof of the house. Then she danced just twice and suddenly flew away right through the roof.

And he went after her to try to overtake her. Out of com-passion she did not travel faster than he could walk. 'Oh, my Peter,' said she, 'return home, since thou canst not overtake me, for I shall not continue out of compassion to go slowly (for she was now with child), but soon I shall travel as swiftly as thought. No bone of thine, no bone of thine, nor of thy father's can reach the land of the immortals, of the three sisters.' 'Go with God', he replied, 'for that is what I wished to know, whence thou comest.'

So she set off and reached her home. As soon as she arrived she gave birth to a boy with two apples of silver in his right hand.

He, the babe's father, went after her and travelled for nine years. And he had not accomplished half his journey when he met a snake on the way. And the snake, what said he? 'Beautiful Peter, do me a kindness, for I have a stag in my mouth; do thou cut off his horns and I will do thee a great favour.' So Peter cut off the creature's horns. Then the snake swallowed the stag. 'Well, Peter, what boon?' 'Do me the favour of bringing me to the Other World.' 'That, to be sure is rather a heavy task, but if it is possible, I will strive to do it all the same. I will strive to beat the sounding-board, for three days and three nights I will strive.'

He beat the board. The ravens came; they came in such numbers that they could not be counted. 'Whence art thou?' 'From the land of the strangers.' 'To the land whence thou comest, thither I desire thee to conduct this man.' 'Dead, I might reach it, but alive never.' 'I do not ask thee to travel by thy wings, but to go with him in his carriage.' 'Then I will go.' And Peter took his seat, after making the sign of the cross with his right hand. 'Remain with God.' 'Go in health.'

And what said the raven? 'Oh, my Peter, climb up and look out: dost thou see a pasture?' He replied that he could scarcely see it. 'To get as far as that we shall have to travel for nine years.' They did not reach it soon: in nine years they arrived.

They alighted and ate and drank. Then they got into their carriage and started once more. They travelled on again. 'Oh, my Peter, climb up and see what is to be seen.' 'A black tract of earth.' 'And what else is to be seen?' 'A pig rooting round with its snout.' 'To arrive there we shall have to travel for 900 years.' They travelled far, far, far—and still farther— and yet they did not reach that spot. Then at last they arrived there, short of breath.

They alighted and ate and drank. Then they arose and travelled farther on from there with God's help. And what said the raven? 'Oh, my Peter, is there a black forest to be seen?' 'I can scarcely see it.' 'To get to that spot we shall have to journey for 2,000 years. Behind that forest is the palace of thy wife, the eldest sister; her palace is on the right hand. She has born thee a son, with two silver apples, both of them in his right hand.' When he reached the forest, there were houses to be seen. 'Oh, my Peter, stop and let us have a

rest.' Because Peter had seen the palace he would not stop:
he hurried on, he drove quicker in order to get there.

When he had covered half the distance he met three devils
fighting for three objects. And one is a wand: when thou
touchest a man with it he is turned into rocky stone. And the
second is a pair of shoes: thou canst cross the water in them
without getting wet. And the third is a cap: in it thou canst
eat with the noblest at table and they will not see thee.

And the devils, what said they? 'Here comes Peter the
Beautiful, let us see which of us he will find in the right, me
or thee or him?' 'Oh, my Peter, to whom dost thou award
these things: this wand, this cap, and the pair of shoes? We
want thee to award them to one of us.' 'That is not what I
want', he answered. 'Do ye go to those three hills, and whoever returns quickest, to him will I give these things.' They
all returned at the same time. 'To whom shall I give them,
when ye return at the same time? Ye had better stand still at
one and the same moment, and he who speaks first to him
will I award them.' All three of them thought that he would
stay there a long time in their company, and therefore did
not speak. 'It would be better for me to slay them.' So Peter
touched them with the wand and turned them into stones.
He seized the three objects.

And he set forth on the road to his wife. He proceeded on
his way. A swarm of ants was passing by, and the King of the
ants, what said he? 'Ho! my Gypsy.' 'I am not a Gypsy, I am
a man. 'What is thy name?' 'He of the Forest.' 'Well, get
back, so that the ants may pass, and I will do thee a great
favour, my Peter.' He drew aside and the ants passed. And
what said their King? 'Here, take this ant's foot, and if evil
come to thee put a flame to the ant's foot and we shall smell
it, and we shall attend, and with small and great will come
to thy rescue with our axes on our backs.'

He went on farther. He came to swarms and swarms of
mice. And the King of the mice, what said he? 'Ho! my
Peter, what is thy name?' 'He of the Forest.' He got out of
their way and the mice passed. When his mice had passed, the
King of the mice said: 'Oh, my Peter, what favour can I do
thee? Here, take this mousetail, and if thou art in any difficulty burn it at a candle and we shall smell it, and pay atten-

tion, and with small and great will come with our axes on our backs, and I will save thee from thy difficulty.'

Farther on he came to an army of bees under a lord, and what said he? 'Ho, Peter, get back so that my host may pass. What is thy name?' 'He of the Forest.' He got back. And the lord, what said he? 'What favour can I do for thee? Let me give thee a foot of one of my bees, and if thou burn it on the fire we shall smell it and with great and small come with our axes, the handles on our backs, and do thee a kindness.'

And the raven said: 'God has brought it to pass that thou hast arrived.' So he drove more quickly and reached his wife's home. And now, what is he to do? He put the cap of invisibility on his head. He arrived at dinner time. His wife was at table, his son was eating with his mother. And he, the boy's father, opened the door and entered in. And he takes a cup of sugared coffee and drank it. Then his son said: 'Oh, mammy, my father has come', for he saw him when he raised his cap. He gave the lad a slap on the back. And what said the boy? 'Mother, he slapped me.' 'Hold thy tongue, for not even a bone of thy father's bone can come hither, so that his sin reaches me.' And she seized him once more by the hair. Then what said he, her husband? 'And why dost thou beat my son?' He doffed his hat from his head.

She sent for her two sisters. The two sisters came. 'And what seekest thou here?' they asked Peter. 'I came for my wife.' 'Stop here and eat and drink for three days and three nights and I will set thee this for a task. Lo! dost thou see that hill that is so high? do thou fell it before daybreak; and that pit that is so deep, thou must level it before daybreak; it must be covered and beaten flat, and I shall cast my eye over it to see whether there is the slightest inequality. The work must be started at night.'

He did not consider that much of a task. He had recourse to the ant's foot, and slept without a care on his mind. They came, all and sundry. 'Oh, my Peter, what dost thou want?' 'Lo! dost thou see that hill that is so high and the deep pit by it? they must be level with the ground before daybreak.' 'Leave it to me', said the King of the ants. 'Speak no further to me, for I know everything; look to thine own business.'

Night fell. They set to like demons and accomplished the

task in a minute. They departed: they did not stop longer away from home than it takes to draw two or three puffs from thy pipe.

The next morning the sisters arose, and the youngest sister of all, what said she? 'Sister, sister, this man is devouring my head. Leave him to me and see what I will do to him.' She then set him the task of felling a forest and piling the wood in front of the palace.

When he heard, he burned the mousetail. He thought that he could not manage the job with the mice alone. So again he kindled a flame for those others, the bees. They came, both great and small, and what said they? 'Oh, Peter the Beautiful, why have ye summoned us?' 'That ye may see what I have to do.' So he set them to work one after the other.

And what did he say? 'Little mice, humming bees, ye have come. Look at that forest of mine! cut it down and cart it away in an instant, pile it up in heaps, and make it all one open field.' The trees were cut and arranged, as Peter said, placed in carts and brought thither.

He summoned them, the three sisters. 'Ho! little sisters.' 'Why hast thou called us here?' He had called them to see his cap. 'The shoes, what are they good for?' 'Thou canst cross the water without wetting thy feet.' 'And the cap, what good is it?' 'Thou canst eat with a noble, and the gentry at table will not perceive thee.' And the sisters asked him: 'Listen! what use is the wand?' 'For my own pleasure, for walking with in my hand.'

Then what did he do in his wrath? He seized his wife and pushed her aside, and placed them, the other two sisters, together. 'Oh, little sisters, why did ye set me to do so very very much work? Stay here.' He touched them with the wand and they were turned into stone. Then he went off to his wife and made a wedding-feast for all the Gypsies.

I came riding on a cock and have told you a fine affair. I have no more to tell.

PIEDMONTESE

Recorded by Paul Bataillard

27. Chiavina the Fair

A captain's son went to sleep beneath a tree near a well and saw in his dream a beautiful unknown girl named Chiavina. This dream so distressed his heart that he would neither eat nor drink.

Seeing their son so disturbed, his parents grew uneasy and his father asked him: 'What ails thee, my son? I pray thee tell me.' And the young man told them of his love, and that he would have to shoe his horse sevenfold with silver shoes before he could find his beloved.

He asked for a blessing from his father. He wandered for six months away from his Gypsies before he got any news of Chiavina. At the end of six months he came to a town where there was a great inn, and while the landlord was preparing his meal the young man asked him if there were any fortune-tellers near by. 'Yes,' he replied, 'they have a castle here: dark girls who come to the inn.'

Whilst he was dining Chiavina arrives at the inn with her maid-servant and wants to tell the young man's fortune. The damsel says to her: 'Chiavina, may this man be thy husband, handsome as he is!' And she answers: 'No, I should not like him, may he rather be thine!'

Meanwhile they recognized one another as Gypsies. And there she and her family abode for six months, eating and drinking at the young man's expense. At the end of that time he asked for Chiavina in marriage. But her parents did not wish to give her to him.

Then the captain's son went off in a rage to sleep beneath a tree near the well. He was slumbering when Chiavina came to the well with her damsel to get some water, and seeing him asleep she pushed back his hair and threw water

125

on his face. Behold, he awakes! He took out his knife, cut off Chiavina's locks, and kissed her. Then she snatched the knife from him, and gave him seventeen cuts on his head.

Chiavina went back to her Gypsies. They saw, the Gypsies saw, that her hair had been cut. They wished to know who had done this. 'You wish to know? Well, I will tell you. It was the captain's son who cut off my hair.'

Then the young man returned to his people. His parents said to him: 'Thou didst go to seek thy beloved and thou hast not brought her back, and we know naught about the matter.' And he replied: 'Come, my people, we must all go there together, the whole family.'

As soon as they arrived, after having travelled for another six months, he hid his people at an inn, and dressed himself as a girl in his sister's clothes, and told everyone that his people were ill at a hospital.

Behold! he goes to the castle, to the home of his beloved. Chiavina, watching him arrive in this disguise, and seeing a young girl in distress, desired her for her sleeping companion. He answered: 'But I am lodging at the inn and I want to sleep there.' So he takes her back with him.

At night they play together and, tired of playing, went to sleep. Said the captain's son to Chiavina: 'Do my hair for me.' She felt his head and found the scars of seventeen gashes. 'Dost thou not remember when thou didst make these cuts on my head?' he asked. She recognized that he was her lover, the captain's son.

In the morning she drew her smock over her head and cried: 'Now I am thine, and to-morrow thou must go to ask for me in marriage.' He went to ask for Chiavina, and her father gave her to him. And they celebrated the wedding of Chiavina the Fair.

GERMAN

Recorded by John Sampson

―――――――――⟨⟡⟩―――――――――

28. The Count's Daughter

Hachares was a count. He had one daughter, a girl of seventeen years. And he would not let her go far afield.

But when she had turned seventeen, she went far afield down to the water-side. And a ferry-boat came to the spot with two robbers aboard. And they stole the count's daughter.

They sought the girl for a whole year but they did not find her. Now near the count there lived a poor young painter. And he said: 'I am going to search for the girl throughout the land. Which way did she go, when she left your house?' And the count pointed out the road the girl had taken towards the water-side. And the painter set forth.

And he stopped close to the spot whence the robbers had borne away the girl. And the same robbers who stole the girl, beat him and carried him off. They bore him off to a great forest.

Now this youth was a very cunning painter. Said the robber chief to him: 'If thou behavest thyself we will not slay thee. I have only one daughter, so do thou swear thou wilt not love her. If my girl says to thee: "Wilt thou not love me?" thou must tell us immediately.' The robber chief went forth to rob.

As soon as the robber chief had departed, his daughter took the youth by the hand and led him into the house, through four-and-twenty doors. Then she took out her pistol. Said she: 'O youth, if thou dost not love me I will shoot thee.' 'I have taken an oath', he answered, 'that I will never love thee.' Said the girl: 'That oath, it counts for nothing at all! If thou takest me I will bear thee away from here. The four-and-twenty thieves only live here for two weeks, and I know thy forest and thy road home.'

The youth took the pistol and shot her in the head. Then her mother appeared and he shot her too. The youth went into room after room, but did not find the count's daughter. He sought her in all the four-and-twenty rooms, and at length in the very last one he found her, the count's daughter, the seventeen-year-old girl, who had been stolen. She was stark naked, without a stitch upon her, and she was well-nigh heart-broken. And the painter knew that this was the girl whom he had sought throughout the land.

And he said to her: 'After thee have I come, and thee have I sought throughout the land, throughout the world. What are we to do now? And how shall we find out whither to go?' And the youth hoisted her on to his back, and took meat and bread with him, and wine and much money, and went with her into the forest.

He did not know which way to go. But he found the great water, and from there they could not go any farther, for the river lay before them. He said to the maiden: 'We cannot cross over yonder so let us stop here. Let us climb into that tall tree and lay us down there to sleep, for the robbers will follow us and find us. Far back in the tree they will not see us.'

The robbers returned from their robbery. They saw that their chief's daughter and his wife had been slain, and the count's girl stolen away. Straightway the robbers went in a dozen different directions to look for the painter, for they knew this youth had killed their chief's wife and daughter and had fled with the count's girl.

The robbers crossed the water by the ferry-boat, and they came upon the same tree where the youth and maiden were sleeping above. They tied up their boat to that same tree in whose branches the pair were lying asleep. Said one robber to his mate: 'Comrade, the youth is bound to come here and the girl with him. He must come here, for where else could he flee? And from here he can go no farther. So I will lay me down here, and do thou, comrade, sleep no longer; for when I get up, then thou canst sleep.'

Now the youth and the maiden were watching these robbers. And the youth took his flask of wine and emptied it into the robber's mouth as he lay asleep. So this man called to his mate: 'Do not pour water into my mouth, but let me sleep for I am weary.' Said the other robber: 'I did not pour water into thy mouth.' 'But thou didst.' And the robbers began to fight together, and one of them slew the other. Then from the tree the youth shot the second robber.

And the youth climbed down from the tree, and the maiden with him, and they seated themselves in the same boat by which the robbers had stolen them both.

And the pair went home to the count, the father of this maiden of seventeen years. And they made ready for their wedding. And the count gave his daughter to the young painter. And if he is not dead he is still alive to this day.

BELGIAN

Recorded by Jan Yoors

29. The Mosquito

In the golden holiness of a night, that will never be seen again and will never come back, there lived in a certain country far, far away at the other side of the great waters, a little mosquito.

You know what a *tzintzari* is, I suppose? Our ancestors of the old days in Prussia and Hungary called him mostly *suggnogi*. They also gave him the name *gindatsa*.

This mosquito, let me tell you, was so conceited that the like of him was never heard of or seen in this world. Everybody hated him for his wickedness. He was constantly boasting about his intelligence. As for beauty he was unequalled in the whole earth, so he said.

Everywhere he passed or paused on the roads the peasant girls and young Gypsies were dying for him. So he said about himself. Even Gypsy women; married and with children—forgive me if I allude to such things in your presence!—fell in love with him.

In a wild country, not very far away, in the heart of dark woods there was an ancient ruined castle. And in this old ruin there lived, all by herself, an old candle that burned eternally.

Numerous were the men who, on hearing of the candle's fabulous reputation, set out for this country to match their strength against hers. But whoever matched themselves in duel with the wretched little candle came back scorched and roasted.

Well! when our mosquito heard all the palaver concerning this business he paused a little in inner speculation.

Then he took a big knife, cut two thick slices of bread, and buttered them generously. He roasted two pieces of meat, peeled three onions, helped himself to three big pimentos and took a pinch of salt.

Then he packed all his provisions in his mother's big golden kerchief, knotted it and went on his way in search of the village where lived the invincible candle.

He choked with anger to think that anyone in the world could be stronger than he was. (And who, young men, told you that he was strong? He was indeed no bigger than a fly.)

He walked for one month, he walked for yet a second month, and in the third month at last he arrived where he wanted to arrive. (Let God strike him in his pride!) Truly the mosquito looked upon himself already as a personage of importance. (May God cause the earth to swallow him!)

He pulled his cap over his eyes, thrust his hands into his pockets, and set out in the direction of the ruined castle, where the candle lived. It did not matter to him how he managed to get there, so he forced his way into the room where he wanted to be.

But when he saw the wee candle standing upright in front of him he was at first taken by surprise. What was he to do now? He coughed very loudly to see what the candle would do. She did not stir. He turned up his nose and whistled. Even now the flame did not budge. Now the mosquito, possessed by the devil, grew furiously angry. His blood was boiling, his heart was beating fiercely, and his eyes were casting sparks.

The candle remained herself: none of this moved her at all. (May the holy God bless her and keep her enemies far away!) She was a church candle, you see, and had come here from a holy place of pilgrimage.

Our mosquito drew close to her and looked down upon her mockingly. She did not condescend to answer anything at all. Our quarrelsome man got more and more enraged, and began to mock her and insult her and her mother as well as herself in a most obscene manner. The candle did not answer; she did not answer.

The mosquito even began to curse the poor candle roundly, for no reason whatsoever. It was impossible for him by any means to make her lose her temper. The candle did not even cast a look at him.

So now he flew into a rage and shrieked at her in Lowari: 'Come outside with me if you are a true man and let us try our strength in duel.' (Let shame devour his face! By what right does he desire the poor little candle to try her strength with him, the more that she has never done him any wrong?)

Then he insults the candle's ancestors, those who are under the earth. He knows no longer what fear is. And she did not speak a single word in reply: only this time her light quivered slightly. When he perceived that nothing was of any avail, neither scorn nor insults, against the memory of her ancestors, he took a step backwards and, in Gypsy style, gave her a blow with his fist under the chin.

'Oh! oh! oh! I have burned myself. Oh! candle, you have devoured my hand. How is it that you did not understand I was only joking with you? Why are you so cruel to me? I was not trying to take advantage of you. I had not a suspicion in my mind of any bad intention towards you.' And there in fear and pain he stood weeping tears as big as my fist. 'Who', he went on, 'would believe that the candle was so strong in very truth? Let me have news of my father's death if she did not appear to me to be faint-hearted!'

The mosquito abandoned the kerchief with his provisions on the spot. He also forgot his cap and scattered his shoes on the way, he ran so fast. He arrived in tears at his mother's and father's.

'What have you done, boy? What have you done, my boy?' And his mother became wild with grief when she saw these burns of his and that he had no hand. His old mother ties a kerchief round her head, took out her pennies which she had hidden inside her mattress, and sets out with her son for the big hospital.

'O great doctor', she said, 'to you I have come that you may heal my son. God grant you luck and health! The money that is required shall be paid to you. Even thick gold sovereigns we will give you, if you are skilful enough and have the ability to replace the hand of my son. Oh, my God! they have ruined my son, ruined him!'

'Your son, Madam, will need a new hand', replied the doctor, 'but where shall we get one? We have only the hands of men. We cannot cure him because we have no mosquito hands to graft on to the limb.' 'Go and search the shops,' said she, 'you may find something that might do.' They went and searched in the town; they asked and begged but they found no hand.

When they realized that it was futile to search further, all the Mosquito tribe gathered together and made the feeble suggestion: 'Why not graft on to our cousin the foot of a fowl?' 'What, the foot of a fowl?' 'Yes truly, Gypsies, the foot of a fowl.'

They went once again to the hospital. (Let it disappear with the night, and let it not trouble my dreams!) And the cleverest surgeons sewed a huge chicken's foot on to the small mosquito.—Good! let us get on!

Well! do you think that this brought the mosquito back to his senses? Not at all! little brother. As soon as his fist was healed and no longer gave him any pain, he took his big knife and . . . Ten times already had the mosquito seen himself vanquished by the candle, and then God allowed him to come to his senses. He no longer sought to pick a quarrel with the poor candle.

When people saw him walking along they stopped in the road to wait for him to pass by them, and then they would shout after him: 'O miracle of a child, who are you? Are you a male or a female? To what class of animal do you belong?' He had now six chicken feet, four chicken wings and also the head and rump of a chicken. And in very truth I must tell you he looked like a miracle of God. The stupid country folk went on their knees in his presence and prayed to him as if he had really been God. Every day his pride increased till his folly turned his head.

Well! one day he was sauntering by some running water and saw the mayor of the village swimming naked in the stream. A vagrant robber had come upon the mayor's clothes, seized them and disappeared. The mayor had now nothing left to cover himself with, and did not dare to go home, naked as he was. He called out to the mosquito and prayed him to help him somehow or other. He promised money, more and more money.

But the mosquito put forward his own views, thus: 'O farmer, help you I can, only on condition that you believe what my mouth says and that you do what I order.' The mayor answered: 'I agree, O master, I agree; act as you consider best.'

Then the malicious mosquito made a barter with the peasant: first of all they exchanged heads, after that their 'behinds' and bellies, and further their hands and feet. And after they had finished, your mosquito looked like a man and the stout mayor was transformed into the miraculous mosquito.

The mosquito who had become a man went to the mayor's palace. He was not used to living in the company of human beings, and therefore felt no shame at all, at walking naked along the streets and passing in this state near to women. The urchins of the whole town ran after him, singing and dancing. They thought he was drunk.

He arrived at the home of the peasant, entered the house, and dressed himself in the most gorgeous clothes of the man. And that is how from a foolish mosquito he became a wise mayor.

Two weeks later his marriage with a rich farmer's daughter took place. About the food and drink we will make no further mention. . . . There was music and dancing and our mosquito enjoyed himself thoroughly.

But now the real peasant arrived to change back again with the mosquito as he wants to become a man as before. The mosquito was already intoxicated, and he was in love with the girl and she too was infatuated with him. Why should he observe the pact he had made with the mayor? If it had occurred to that fool of a farmer to put so much faith in him, it must have been God who had duped him!

Wine was flowing freely and the guests were drinking hard. But the old farmer maddened them so much by insisting on talking and talking that everyone present grew infuriated with him. Who could believe him when he said that he was the real mayor?

The young woman, who had been his own betrothed before, wrung his neck, and they roasted him over the fire and devoured him at the wedding feast.

I was there also, hiding under the table, and I heard everything and I saw everything. As I was famished I secretly tried to snatch a morsel of the six-legged chicken, for myself and for my old mother. But the farmers perceived me and forced me to flee. That is the only reason why I cannot give you a proof of the truth of my story. But all the same I came to tell it to you, in the hope that it would give you pleasure and help to pass away your time.

SECTION TWO

TALES TOLD IN THE VERNACULAR
BY GYPSY NARRATORS

ENGLISH

*Recorded by T. W. Thompson from Noah Lock
and Others*

———————◆———————

30. The Robber and the Housekeeper

The' was wonst a big high gentleman what lived in a fine
mansion, a very grand place it was an' no mistake, standing
back in its own grounds, an' the' was a carriage drive leading
up to it from the road, an' trees growing all about it. I can't
tell you exac'ly who he was, but he was some very high
notified gentleman. Now it so come about at the time I'm
a-speaking on as this gentleman, an' the lady his wife, an'
their son—they only had but one son—an' their two da'ghters, they all went away for a week's holiday. An' they had a
little baby, this gentleman an' lady had, but they didn't take
it wid 'em; they left it at home wid the housekeeper; an' they
left one 'n the sarvant gals as well for comp'ny like for the
housekeeper, but the tother sarvant gals they took wid 'em.

They'd be gone away now some two or three days, when
the' comes knocking at the doar 'n the house an owld woman
—or so sh'd 'pear to be—a rale comital owld woman. An'
this owld woman got a-gate telling tales an' things, an' sich
funny tales she towld that she kept the housekeeper an' the
tother sarvant in fits o' laughing. She got on an' got on, one
tale a'ter another, an' all the time they was standing at the
back doar, all the three 'n they. Whatsumever, a'ter a bit,
the one sarvant says to the tother: 'Shall we ax her to come
in an' sit down a bit?' 'Well, aye', says the tother, 'she'll be a
bit o' good comp'ny for we.' So they axes her in, an' sets
vittles afoare her—plenty to eat an' drink—an' a'ter when
she'd had a bellyful they all sits talking, an' telling tales, an'
laughing till nigh upon night time.

So whatever to you, the owld woman now begins to ax 'em
for one bit o' thing an' another, an' they gi'es her these, for

they wa'n't o' no value not to speak on. Getting bowld-like she axes 'em for summat else, an' this thing it was o' some value, though what it was exac'ly I couldn't rightly say—not now. Whatsumever, it was kept upstairs, this thing was what she'd axed for, so the sarvant an' the housekeeper as well they both goes upstairs, an' they leaves the little baby downstairs in the kitchen wid the owld woman. Whether it was they couldn't find it, or whether it was they was talking it over a bit as to how they should get rid 'n this owld woman, or what, I couldn't say, but they was a t'emendous long while upstairs, an' the owld woman gets out o' patience wid waiting. 'If you don't come down at wonst,' she hollers out, 'an' bring me that thing what I axed you for, than I shall restroy this baby.' Whatsumever, they 'pears to take no notice on her, so she makes for the baby, an' is just going to knock its brains out, when out jumps a big, black 'triever dog, as had been sleeping in the corner wid one eye open all the time, an' which she'd never as much as noticed afoare. It has her by the throat afoare she could stir hand or limb to keep it off, an' shakes the life out'n her—aye, kills her stone dead on the spot it does.

As soon as they hears the baby scream the housekeeper an' the tother sarvant they comes rushing downstairs, an' they finds the owld woman lying dead on the floar, an' the big 'triever dog standing over her. Now being as she is dead they begins to sarch her, an' what should they find out but that the owld woman isn't a woman at all, but a man dressed up in woman's things. There's something suspicious about this, they thinks, an' they goes through all his pockets, an' there they finds a 'volver—a six chamber 'volver—a dagger, and a horn.

Whatsumever to you, the housekeeper now takes and blows this horn, three times she blows it, an' no sooner has she done this but what three robbers comes running up the drive as fast as ever they can. She doesn't lose not a minute; she snatches up the 'volver and shoots two 'n they dead on the spot, an' the third she'd have sarved the same, only but he run away agen afoare she had the time.

Now when the master an' mistress come home agen it was only nat'ral-like 'at the first thing they should ax was, how had their little baby been this long time. 'Oh! quite well', says the housekeeper, for she didn't like to say nothink about the robbers. But the tother sarvant she wasn't agen telling, so she up an' towld the whole story. When the master heeard this he was very pleased at the way the housekeeper had done to the robbers. He should make her comfor'able for the rest 'n her life, he said, an' she should have a house 'n her own near by to his, an' no more work to do, that was not unless she had a mind to, an' she shouldn't want for nothink, he said, as long as he had money to buy it wid. So soon a'ter he had a very tidy soart 'n a house builded in his own grounds, an' this he gi'ed to the housekeeper for her very own, to do as she liked wid.

Whatever to you, the robber as had run away an' missed getting killed, he put a 'vartisement into the papers saying as how he'd like to find a job as coachman wid some gentleman; he was very used to horses, he said, and a good stidy driver. Now it just so happened as the gentleman what lived in the mansion next to the one where the housekeeper was stood in want 'n a coachman, so when he seen the 'vartisement into the papers he sent for the robber, an gi'ed him a month's trial, an' when the month was up he took him on for good.

Afoare long this robber gets on wid the housekeeper, and goes courting her very strong. An' she gets rale sweet on him, her not knowing like who he is, for he was a very good-looking man, an' pleasant spoken enough when it suited his parpose. A'ter a bit he axes her, will she marry him. She doesn't say 'yes', nor yet she doesn't say 'no', but she goes straight to her master an' tells him all, an' axes him: 'what shall I do?' 'Oh! that's soon answered', he says. 'If you're fond 'n him,' he says, 'then marry him. But if you don't like him,' he says, 'then don't marry him.' 'Oh! I love him', she says. 'Well then,' he says, 'that being the state o' 'fairs, you go an' tell him you'll have him.' So she did, and afoare long they got married, an' went to live in the house what the gentleman 'd had builded for her.

At first they was very happy, of course, like everybody is. About six months passed, an' then one day the robber tells his wife as he's going to take her to see his delations. 'You know, my dear,' he says, 'we now been married this long time, an' I ha'n't as much as set eyes on one 'n my own people from that day to this. They must think it strange 'n we not going over to see 'em.' 'Yes dear,' she says, 'we ought to go, and I'm sure it'll be a great pleasure to me.' 'It will', he says, and away he goes to harness the pony, an' yoke it. She gets into the trap besides him, and off they sets.

He drives on and on over mountains and all manner o' wild lonesome places all that day, and all the next day, and all the day a'ter that agen. About the fourth day she begins to be a bit anazy in her mind, an' wonders, poor thing, wher-ever they can be going to, an' whenever will they get there. She works herself up into sich a state till at last she bursts out crying; she couldn't keep it in no longer. 'Oh! my dear husband,' she says, 'where are we going to, an' however much farther is it?' 'Be quiet, woman,' he says, 'you'll find out just now; an' plenty soon enough that'll be, for if you only knew what was to happen to you when we get to my brother's house you wouldn't be fretting your heart out to get there.' 'Oh! my dear,' she says, 'whatever is up with you talking so strange-like.' 'Well, if you will know,' he says, 'it was you murdered my two brothers, and now we're a-going to take us vengeance on you.' At that she begun crying agen, an' begging him on her bended knees to take her back home, but he didn't take not a bit o' notice on her, only towld her to stop her hollering, or it would be the worse for her.

In about another day they comes to the robbers' house, an' the robbers they takes an' shuts up the housekeeper in a room, an' strips her stark mother naked, an' ties her up to the ceiling by the hairs 'n her head, an' leaves her there, whils' they go an' talk over what kind o' death they shall put her to. Whatsumever, they hadn't tied her hands, so as soon as they're gone out 'n the room she gets to work breaking her hairs, two or three at a time, bit by bit, till at last she works herself loose. She opens the window as quiet as ever she can, an' Lord! she was a-frightened for fear they should hear her, but they didn't, so she gets out. She takes a good look round to make cartain as nobody is watching her, an' then away she runs as fast as her legs can take her, away back on the road they'd come.

Whatever to you, she might be gone from the robbers' house p'r'aps three or four hours, an' she was fair fit to drop, an' all of a faint, when she comes up wid an owld man driving a cart full o' nothink but apples. An' she towld this owld man 'bout the state she was in—which there wa'n't no need for, as he'd got eyes an' could see for hisself—an' how she was running away from some robbers as was going to take her life, an' where it was she was wanting to get to. 'Oh!' she says, 'if only you could find it in your heart to do a kindness to a poor woman in trouble, an' help her on her way a bit!' The owld man was very sorry for her, an' so, being as he was going her road, he towld her to jump up besides him, which she did pretty quick as you can guess. An' he shifts the apples away from one side 'n the cart, an' tells her to lay herself down there, an' she does, an' he covers her all over wid the apples.

He drives on now, an' for about two days they goes on and on over the mountains an' places, an' never sets eyes on a soul. Then a fine gentleman on horseback comes up wid they. It was the robber this was, an' the owld man knowed it well enough, for he was a cunning owld fellow. He'd heeard the horse coming along behind him all the while, but he hadn't as much as turned round. 'My good man,' says the robber, 'have you seen annythink on a woman going stark mother naked?' 'N—o' the owld man answers him, an' goes on driving on. 'But she's come this road', says the robber, 'an' she must ha' passed you somewheres, for she isn't behind you.' The owld man pulls up. 'Well,' he says, 'now I come to think 'n it, I seen somethink yesterday what looked very funny; I couldn't make nothink on it. Something white it was, 'way back on the owld road right over yonder, miles an' miles back. What it was though I couldn't say, I'm sure.' 'Ah!' says the robber, 'that must ha' been her', an' wi' that he puts spurs to his horse, an' gallops off to look for her down the owld side road, what was many an' many a mile back.

The owld man laughs to hisself an' goes on agen, an' he gets a long way afoare the robber comes up wid him a second time. 'Stop, you owld white-headed rascal', he shouts—the robber does, cussing an' swearing somethink awful; 'you been telling me lies for a parpose.' 'No,' says the owld man, 'that

I ha'n't, for I ha'n't never towld you no lies at all.' 'Well, anyhow,' says the robber, 'the woman ha'n't gone that road what you towld me.' 'Well, I never said as she had', says the owld man, very quiet-like. 'All I said was I seen some funny white thing along the owld road. It was you yourself', he says, 'as said it must be her.' 'Ah,' says the robber, 'I can see you got moare knowledge on her nor what you lets on, you owld varmint. I shouldn't wonder if you ha'n't got her in your cart all the time.' 'No, I ha'n't,' says the owld man; 'but if you don't put no trust in my words p'r'aps you'll believe your own eyes. Look,' he says, an' he pulls off the cover 'n his cart, an' shows the robber his cart full of apples. 'She's not here, is she now?' 'No,' says the robber, 'I can't see no-think only but apples.' Then a'ter this the robber leaves him, an' the owld man drives on now till he comes to the place where the housekeeper lives.

Whatever to you, the first thing the housekeeper does is to go an' tell her owld master everythink what has happened to her, an' she begs him to save her from the robber. 'My dear,' he says very kind-like, 'don't you think no moare about it. You must stay here', he says, 'in my house, an' you shall have everythink what you wants—plenty to eat an' to drink, an' plenty o' grand clothes to wear, an' a lady companion to be wid you always. And as for the robber,' he says, 'just leave him to me; I'll see to it as he don't do you no harm. I got a plan for catching him', he says; 'it's just now come into my head.'

An' wid that he goes off, an' orders bills to be put out everywheres, on every barn-door, and every tree, and every gate-post for miles an' miles round, saying as on sich-an'-sich a day he'll give a big feast, and as everybody is axed to it, rich an' poor, they'll all be made welcome. Now it gets on an' gets on till it's only but two days afoare the feast is to be gi'ed, when the robber he comes back agen into them parts, an' of course it's not long till he sees the bills. He goes to his wife's house, but it's empty. Well, he thinks it over to hisself, as the best he can do is to reguise hisself an' go to this feast; she is sure to be there, he thinks, an' he can watch her where she goes a'ter when it's over.

On the night 'n the feast there is the housekeeper, all

dressed in silks an' satins, an' her lady companion at her side, walking up an' down, up an' down, in the grand hall where the supper is laid. An' the master he is standing at the doar shaking hands wid everybody as they comes in. Of course, they're both 'n looking out for the robber. Now it's a curious thing that though they seen everybody as come in they didn't see the robber among 'em, neither the one nor yet the tother didn't. And agen when all the guests is sat down to the tables they both walks back'ards an' far'ards, an' back'ards an' far'ards, an' they has a good look at everybody, an' yet they can't find him, though they know as he must be in the room somewheres. 'Well, this is uncommon strange', says the master; 'but I'll find him yet afoare the night is out, just you see.'

Now a'ter when they'd all eaten till they couldn't eat no more, an' drunk most all the wine, the master he gets up from his place, an' he begins to make a bit 'n a speech. 'I been greatly pleased', he says, 'wid your company here to-night. An' now,' he says, 'afoare you go—and I shall be very sorry to have to part from you—the's just the one thing. I'm now going to call for a toast,' he says, 'which I wants *all* 'n you here present, *every one'n you*, to drink standing up, *wid your left hands flat open above your heads*, so.' It was a cunning trick this was, for the robber you see had the two first fingers 'n his left hand cut off by the middle joints, so that when they all stood up an' raised their hands to drink the toast he was f'un out. The master tells his sarvants to seize him, an' he sends to fatch a rigiment o' soldiers, an' they comes, an' they shoots him. An' that was the end 'n the robber.

31. Clever Pat

The' was wonst a big lord—a king he was in fact—what put a 'vartisement into the papers, saying as how he was in want of a man, an' this man he was to be a 'spicially good driver. Now this king he had a very crooked road, an' it was very narrow as well this road was, an' falled away right steep on both sides: he'd had it made this way on parpose. Whatever to you, an Englishman an' an Irishman replies for the job. An' first the Englishman comes. 'Can you drive?' the king axes him. 'Yes, sir,' he says, 'I think I can drive pretty well.' 'That won't do' says the king; 'you must *know*.' Whatsumever, he gi'es him a carriage an' pair, and tells him to drive along this crooked road 'n his. He starts off, the Englishman does, driving very careful—he was a good stidy driver, mind, an' knowed how to handle a pair o' horses—but he hadn't gone far afoare he has the carriage over, an' it an' the horses an' all goes rowling down the bank by the side 'n the road. Then the Irishman comes. 'Can you drive?' the king axes him. 'Yes, yer honour,' says Pat, 'I can drive on the top 'n a needle as straight as a pin.' So the king sets him the same to do as the Englishman had failed at. Now Pat he starts off full gallop, an' he does it as azy as winking. 'That's very good,' says the King, 'an' you're a won'erful clever fellow.'

'Now what else is the' you can do?' he axes Pat. 'Oh!' says Pat, 'I can do annythink in the world, yer honour.' 'Well then,' says the king, 'go an' count all my cattle an' sheep.' 'Right ye are, yer honour', says Pat, an' away he goes. Now a'ter a bit he comes back wid the number, and tells it to the king. 'The's sich-an-such a number, yer honour,' he said. 'No,' says the king, 'that won't do at all: it's ten behind.' 'Shure, yer honour,' says Pat, 'an' why not ten in front?' 'You don't take my meaning,' says the king. 'It's ten too few.' 'Oh! now I see, yer honour,' says Pat, 'I ha'n't f'un 'em all.' 'That's it,' says the king. 'But have you looked', he axes, 'in that little wood over yonder? They sometimes get there, leastways the cattle does, for sake 'n the flies.' Pat hadn't looked there, so away he goes, an' he hunts about, an' he hunts about, till he finds all save one. Presently, he comes back, an' he tells the king as he's now f'un' all the tothers saving one. 'That won't do,' says the king, 'not yet: you must find the one what is missing.'

Now Pat was just going off agen when the king calls him back. 'Pat,' he says, 'to-night I'm to hold a grand ball, at nine o'clock,' he says, 'an' I want you to come an' throw eyes at me, so as to g'ie me a bit of ancouragement like when I'm dancing wid the ladies.' 'Very good, yer honour,' says Pat, 'I shall be there.' 'An' now, Pat,' says the king, 'you must

come an' have somethink to eat an' drink,' an' he takes Pat
an' gi'es him vittles an' drink, plenty an' to spare. Now a'ter
when he has a bellyful, what does Pat do but goes an' cuts
the eyes out 'n all the king's cattle an' sheep, an' stuffs his
pockets cram full o' these eyes till they're bulging out, an'
won't hold not another one.

So whatever to you, just afoare nine o'clock Pat goes into
the ballroom wid these eyes in his pocket, an' as soon as ever
the king catches sight 'n him he nods an' winks to Pat, an'
Pat nods and winks back at him. Then he comes over to
where Pat is stood, the king does, an' 'minds him what he's
got to do. 'You'll be sure,' he says, 'an' throw eyes at me
every time as I comes past wid a lady.' 'You can trust me for
that, yer honour,' says Pat.

It wa'n't long now afoare the musicianers starts playing,
an' the dancing begins. The king comes round tripping it
wid some grand lady, an' as he passes close by to Pat, Pat
puts his hand in his pocket, an' pulls out an eye, an' throws
it at him. An' the king he winks an' smiles at Pat very
pleased-like, an' Pat he winks an' smiles back at the king.
Now a'ter this the same thing happens every time as the
king comes round, till Pat he ha'n't not a single eye left; an'
the floor got that slippy wid all the eyes Pat had throwed 'at
the dancers started tum'ling down. Now a'ter when the ball
is over, an' all the guests is gone, the king he comes to Pat.
'Pat,' he says, 'that was very nice indeed: you throwed eyes
at me ancommon well.' 'Yes, yer honour,' says Pat, 'your
own sheep's an' cattle's.' But the king didn't take his meaning a bit, though he thought it a very funny saying.

Whatsumever to you, next morning the king sends for Pat
agen. 'Pat,' he says, 'if you can bring all my cattle an' sheep
together into the yard here an' count 'em back'ards, then,' he
says, 'you shall have my da'ghter.' So Pat goes, an' he gathers
all the king's cattle an' sheep together into the yard, an'
begins counting 'em back'ards. An' the king he comes out to
inspect 'em. First of all he goes to his prize bull. 'Oo-h! ! !' he
says as soon as ever he sets eyes on it. 'Whatever is up? Here's
my prize bull wid its two eyes cut out!' Then he goes an' he
looks at all the tothers, an' he finds ne'er a one 'n they but
what has its two eyes cut out. An' he calls for Pat to come.

'However can sich a thing have happened, Pat?' he axes. 'I've never heeard in all my life of annythink like it.' 'Well, yer honour,' says Pat, 'if you mind it rightly you towld me to throw eyes at you at the ball last night.' 'Yes,' says the king, 'I did.' 'An' shure, yer honour,' says Pat, 'wherever should I get so many eyes 'cepting from your own cattle an' sheep.' 'You fool,' says the king, 'what I meant for you to do was to wink an' smile at me an' that. But now,' he says, 'for this thing what you done—blinded all my cattle an' sheep— you shall be 'headed.'

So whatever to you, it wa'n't so very long afoare the king sent for Pat agen. 'Pat,' he says, 'I'm going to giv' you one moare chance; I'm going to set you', he says, 'one moare thing to do, an' if you comes through all right, then I shan't have you 'headed, an' you shall marry my da'ghter just the same; but if you don't,' he says, 'then for cartain you shall be 'headed.' 'Yer honour is very good to me', says Pat. 'An' now what is it yer honour would set me to do?' 'Well,' says the king, 'I got five pigeons, an' the task you must reform is to catch these pigeons—all the five 'n they, mind, an' a'ter when you catched 'em you got to bring 'em an' show 'em to me.' An' he axed Pat if he un'erstood his meaning this time, an' Pat said as he did. Now these here five pigeons was his five da'ghters what had been 'chanted.

Well, the first thing Pat does is to fill his pockets full wid corn, an' then he goes into the barn, an' he throws down a few grains near by to the doar. Two 'n the pigeons comes an' eats this, so Pat throws 'em a bit moare farther in, an' then a bit moare farther in agen, till he 'tices 'em right in. Then he does the same by the tother three, an' all the while he keeps throwing a bit o' corn to the ones as he's got in, till at last he has all the five 'n they inside the barn. Still he goes on feeding 'em, a bit at a time, an' then a bit moare, an' wid every lot he throws down he creeps a bit nearer to the doar, till in the end he has 'em safe shut in. Then he catches the five pigeons an' puts 'em in a basket, an' off he goes wid 'em to the king. An' he is pleased wid hisself for sure

The king is standing in his big hall wid his sword in his hand ready to 'head Pat. 'Well, Pat,' he says, 'have you catched 'em?' 'Yes, yer honour,' says Pat. 'But have you catched all the five 'n they?' the king axes. 'Yes, yer honour,' says Pat. 'I got the lot here in this basket.' 'Well, open it, then,' the king tells him, 'an' let me see for myself.' So Pat opens the basket, an' the pigeons flies out. The king counts 'em. 'The's only but four here, Pat,' he says. 'Faith, yer honour,' says Pat, 'I catched all the five 'n they.' 'That don't signify,' says the king; 'you've only fatched me four. You must go an' fatch me the tother one,' he says, 'or I shall 'head you.'

Now Pat, he wa'n't telling no lies: he had catched all the five 'n they right enough; but one 'n the king's da'ghters had fell in love wid him, see? an' she was that shy 'n him 'at somehow or another she'd got away from him agen a'ter when he'd put her in the basket.

Whatever to you, Pat now goes to catch this one pigeon what was missing, an' he tries an' he tries for two or three days till at last he gets it. Then he takes it to the king, an' the king he's very pleased, an' says as he shall make a big feast in honour 'n the 'casion.

Now a'ter when the king has gone out 'n the room, this pigeon it flies an' parches itself on the throne, and when Pat looks what does he see sitting there but the most beautiful lady you ever set eyes on, all dressed in fine clothes an' jewels, an' wid a gowlden crown on her head. An' she speaks to Pat, 'Pat,' she says, 'you're the luckiest man in the world, for I fell in love wid you as soon as ever I set eyes on you.'

Well, soon a'ter that Pat was married to the king's da'ghter, an' the owld king he gi'ed up his palace an' all his lands to Pat an' his da'ghter, an' they lived happy there in the palace ever a'ter.

32. The Lady in Want of a Husband

Once on a time, when I was a handsome young fellow, an' that ain't bin so very long ago as you can see, I was tekking a walk down the street into this very town o' Nottingham when I sin big notices up everywheres, an' heeard the bellman crying, as how some grand lady was in want of a husband. Very good-looking she was s'posed to be, an' had no end o' money: in fact I believe she was a princess. So I ta'en pertic'lar note'n what sort of a man it was she wanted. Dark he had to be, an' very handsome; not too tall, nor yet too short. That's just me, I thought to myself; an' so it was, mind you—exac'ly my describance. Thinks I to myself then, I'll go to-morrow an' reply for this job, 'specially as she's got plenty o' money, for that's a thing I can do wi'.

Howsoever, I got talking wi' some men in the street, an' towld 'em my intention. 'Don't you go,' they says, 'for she's had seven husbands already, this lady has, an' there's nobody knows what's become on 'em. Ne'er a trace'n any a one of 'em is to be found,' they says. Well, I thought, that don't sound nice; but all the same I'll venture. She won't find me as easy to get rid on as these tothers.

So next day I went an' replied. A maid-servant answered the door, an' axed me had I come to marry the missis. 'Yes,' I says, 'if she's willing.' She went an' towld the lady I was waiting; an' presently she come back to say as I was to go in an' let her—that's the missis—have a look at me. In I went as bowld as brass. Yes, I'd do fine, she said: in fact I was just the very man she was wanting. An' a day or two after—to cut my story short—we was married. A grand wedding an' all we had, I can tell you.

The first night we was together I woke up very early: about the middle'n the night it must ha' bin. My missis wa'n't there. This is very queer, I thought. Howsoever, I turned over an' went to sleep agen; an' next time I wakened up there she was right enough. It was nearly getting-up time by then. 'Well, my dear,' I says, 'an' have you had a good night?' 'Yes, thank you,' she says. 'An' you?' 'Very good, thank you, my dear,' I says. The second night it was just the same. By then I was a bit suspicious: I would be, wouldn't I? So the third night I foxed; I didn't go to sleep at all. It would be about the middle'n the night when she slips out o' bed, dresses herself very quietly, puts on some soft slippers, an' goes creeping, creeping downstairs. I followed wi'out letting her see me. She goes pid-padding out'n the house, an' down a little path till she comes to some graves. There is one wi' the soil all loose. She scoops this away wi' her hands, an' gets right down into the grave. I crept close up.

There she is, sitting eating little bits o' flesh an' bone. 'Hello! my dear,' I says; 'an' what might you be eating of?'
'CORPSE, YOU WRETCH, CORPSE!'

33. The Sevenfold Liar

I was going along the road once, an' I may say as I'd nivver bin on this road before. An' first I met wi' a deaf an' dumb man. 'How far might it be to the next village, mister?' I axes him. 'It'll be a tidy step,' he says, 'mebbe three or fower miles.' I goes on, an' next I met wi' a blind man. 'What might the time be, mister?' I axes him. He looks at his watch: 'I mek it twenty minutes to three', he says. Agen I goes on, an' after a bit I met wi' a naked man. Come that time I was badly in want of a smoke, an' I hadn't no 'bacca. 'Can you spare me a pipe o' 'bacca, mister?' I axes him. 'Yes,' he says, 'you can fill up an' welcome.' An' he teks his pouch from his pocket, an' hands it to me for me to help mysel.'
Well, I was all right then. In fact it wa'n't long afore I come to this village. There the first thing I sin was a man wi' no arms wheeling a sack o' 'taters down the street in a wheelbarrow. An' the next thing I sin was a man wi' no legs running after him as hard as ever he could, hollering: 'Stop thief, stop thief; them's my 'taters you'm taking.' A fair to-do there was, an' after when it's over, I goes on agen, an' what should I see now but a very owld man, more'n a hundred years owld. An' the poor owld fellow was crying. 'What's up, gaffer?' I axes him. 'It's my grandfather', he says; 'I bin living wi' him', he says, 'this year or two back. But now he's got married agen', he says, 'an' he's kicked me out'n the house.' I was right sorry for him, but on I goes agen, an' when I got just past the church I met wi' a dead man as they was taking to bury. An' when he sin me he sort o' reckernized me, though mind you I'd nivver bin in this place afore. 'Here's a man', he says, 'as could do wi' a pint o' beer.' An' that' the truth, that is. In fact truer words was nivver spoken.

34. The Basketmaker's Donkey

Once upon a time, when the most part of Gypsies used to travel wid pack-donkeys, there was an owld man as had had the same donkey for years and years; an' being as he'd had it for so long it was a great pet o' his'n. Well, one day this owld man was at home to the place meking a basket or two for his wife to tek round wid her when she went calling. That was mostly what his occoopation, basket-making, was, though sometimes he'd cut a few pegs or a gross or two o' skewers. You know the sort o' man, Rai; not one'n our class o' people, but he could talk a bit o' Romani, an' in a way o' speaking you might call him a Gypsy.

Well, as I was a-saying, this owld man was at home to the place one day busying hisself weaving a basket. An' the moke was wid him, same as it offen was, only instead o' just keeping him company, like what it used to do, it was moidering of him all the while, first one way, then another; meking itself a reg'lar noosance it was. He'd druv it away three or fower times, aye, more'n that, but no sooner had he settled down to his basket but what it was back agen. So at last he gets right angry wid it, an' picks up a long switch as was lying handy. He chases it wid this, an' soon as he gets up wid it he lets fly for all he is worth. It was a tidy big welt he caught it I can tell you, and, believe me, he cuts it clean in two from head to tail, an' the two halves tumbles to the ground, the one this way an' the tother the opposite.

When the poor owld man sin what he'd gone an' done he was fair beside hisself, him being so mortal fond'n the donkey, an' not having another to tek his bits o' things about. 'What can I do?' he says, 'what can I do?' An' the tears was rowling down his face. 'Oh! whatever can I do?' he says. Then he bethinks hisself, all of a sudden-like, of the willow withes he has back to the place, an' he runs an' fetches an armful. An' he stands the two halves'n the donkey up, an' fits the one to the tother, an' binds the two halves together wid the willow withes. Then he goes an' gets some clay, an' he daubs it all along the joining; caulks the two halves together he does. 'There now,' he says, 'I reckon I've med a good job o' that.'

He had an' all, for the two halves'n the donkey growed together agen, an' he'd a many year's service out'n it after that: in fact it lasted him his life. What is more, the willow withes took root an' growed as well, so ever after, whenever he wanted to mek a basket, he didn't have to go searching for withes; he al'ays had a stock ready to hand just for the cutting.

35. Appy Boswell's Monkey

Appy had a monkey, which he'd kept for ten years, an' fed on the best o' everythink, an' done well by in every way. Now this monkey it would never once talk wid him, nor answer his questions, nor even yet as much as say: 'Thank you' when he gi'ed it its vittles.

Whatever to you, one day when Appy had sat hisself down by the side 'n a brick-kiln, the monkey being wid him, a thought come to him about it defusing to speak wid him. 'Well,' he says to hisself, 'come what will I'll make the beggar talk.' So over he goes to the kiln, an' there he finds an oven what is empty, but red scorching hot. Now what does he do but he takes the monkey, an' puts it inside this oven, an' claps a sheet o' iron over the mouth 'n it so as it can't get out. Whatsumever, a'ter about five or ten minutes o' this the monkey begins squealing. 'No mortal man could stand this,' it calls out to Appy, 'so for why should you expect me to? Anlease me, or I shall die.' At this Appy opens the doar. 'Will you promise as you'll talk wid me for the future', he axes it, 'an' answer my questions?' 'Yes, I'll promise', the monkey answers, an' so Appy lets it come out agen now.

So whatever to you, when Appy got home that night he says to his wife: 'Anis,' he says, 'the monkey spoke well wid me to-day, an' so now', he says, 'I'm a-going to treat him well.' He goes an' he makes it a big bowl full of eatables— the best what he had—an' sets this afoare it. Then a'ter when it has eaten its full he axes it, 'Have you enjoyed your vittles?' but it doesn't answer him not a word; it only nods its head. Then he axes it: 'Have you had a bellyful?' but agen it won't answer him not a word. 'Oh! very well then,' says Appy; 'you won't answer me, won't you? Then I shall take you back to that place agen.' Now the monkey, as soon as ever it heears this, it comes for'ard, an' it puts out its hand, an' it strokes Appy on his cheek. 'I'll answer you anny-think', it says, 'if only you'll not take me back there agen.'

36. Down Underground

This is a tale as Lander Smith used to tell about hisself; an' for foolishness an' lies I don't think as Appy Boswell could beat it. He'd get agate talking the owld lead-mining shafts there is into parts o' Derbyshire; sensible talk it would be, mind you, to begin wi'. But after when he'd bin talking a bit, he'd start up all of a sudden summat like this:

'Once when I was into dem parts,' he'd say, 'I was teking a walk over de hills when de dog put up a hare, an' wi' me watching of it, an' not looking where I was a-going, I tum'led down one'n dese *ratvali* shafteses. It was only but a very narrow one, just big enough for a man to get down; an' all de while I was falling I kep' hitting first agen de one side and den agen de tother till I was knocked proper senseless. But at last I come to de bottom, an' right glad I was an' all you may bet. Every bone into my body was broke, but being as I was down underground I thinks to myself as I might as well see what manner o' place it was as I'd got to. So I picks myself up, an' starts out on my travels.

'Everythink was very different to what it was up here. Afore long I come to a nice little lake o' water, an' dere was a man wi' a team o' horses ploughing of it so as he could plant it wi' corn. Den I come to a gentleman's park, an' be hanged if dere wa'n't a ship sailing on it. An' after dat I got into a turnpike road, an' first I met wi' a donkey riding on to a man's back. It was beating of him summat awful, so I towld it if it didn't stop I'd knock its *ratvali* head off; an' it did stop, anyways as long as I was watching of it. Den I lighted on a poor owld roadman: he was sitting breking stones wi' a feather. An' after when I'd left him I come to a small little house, an' dere I sin a woman fetching water into a riddle. I was getting a bit hungry by den, so I axed her could she gi' me a bite o' summat to ate. She said as she'd plenty o' black-puddings if dem would do; an' I said as dey'd do fine. So she took me into de garden, an' showed me a tree where dere was a won'erful fine crop'n 'em, an' said as I could help myself to as many as I pleased.'

I don't know what else he didn't say—Lander, I mean; but the end of it was as he met wi' some Gypsies, and come back agen wi' them. 'We had to go over de sea', he said, 'de way what dey took, but come mid-day we fun a nice place to light a bit o' fire an' have us some vittles. It was pretty near dark when we landed up on de tother side, an' I wondered wherever we'd got to. Den I sin some kilns an' pot-banks, an' I says to myself as dis must be Stoke. An' so it was right enough. An' dere was my owld woman a-waiting for me; an' right glad she was to see me I can tell you after when I'd bin away for so long.'

Recorded by John Sampson
from Johnny and Wasti Gray

37. De Little Bull-Calf

Centers of yeahs ago, when all de most part of de country wur a wilderness place, deah wuz a little boy lived in a pooah bit of a poverty *ker*, an' dis boy's father guv him a deah little bull-calf. De boy used to tink de wurl' of dis bull-calf, an' his father gived him everything he wanted fur it.

Afterward dat his father died, an' his mother got married agin, an' dis wuz a werry wicious stepfather an' he couldn't abide dis little boy, an' at last he said, if de boy bring'd de bull-calf home agin, he wur a-goin' to kill it. Dis father should be a willint to dis deah little boy, shouldn't he, my Sampson?

He used to gon out tentin' his bull-calf every day wid barley bread, an' arter dat, deah wus an ole man comed to him, an' we have a deal of thought who dat wuz, *hoi*? An' he d'rected de little boy: 'You an' youah bull-calf had better go away an' seek youah forchants.'

So he wents an, an' wents an, as fur as I can tell you to-morrow night, an' he wents up to a farmhouse an' begged a crust of bread, an' when he comed back he broked it in two, and guv half an it to his little bull-calf.

An' he wents an to another house, an' begs a bit of cheese crud, an' when he comed back, he wants to gin half an it to his bull-calf. 'No!' de little bull-calf says, 'I'm a-goin' acrost dis field into de wild wood wilderness country, where dere'll be tigers, lepers, wolfs, monkeys, an' a fiery dragin, an' I shall kill dem every one excep' de fiery dragin, an' he'll kill me.' (De Lord could make any animal speak dose days. You know trees could speak onst. Our blessed Lord he hid in de eldon bush, an' it tell't an him, an' he says, 'You shall always stink', and so it always do; but de ivy let him hide into it, and he says: 'It should be green both winter an' summer.')

An' dis little boy did cry, you'ah shuah, and he says, 'Oh! my little bull-calf, I hope he won't kill you.' 'Yes, he will,' de little bull-calf says, 'an' you climb up dat tree, an' den no one can come anigh you but de monkeys, an' ef dey come de cheese crud will sef you. An' when I'm kilt de dragin will go away fur a bit, an' you come down dis tree, an' skin me, an' get my biggest gut out, an' blow it up, an' my gut will kill everything as you hit wid it, an' when dat fiery dragin come, you hit it wid my gut, an' den cuts its tongue out.' (We know deah were fiery dragins dose days, like George an' his dragin in de Bible, but deah! it arn't de same wurl' now. De wurl' is tun'd ovah sence, like you tun'd it ovah wid a spade!)

In course he done as dis bull-calf tell't him, an' he climb't up de tree, and de monkey climb't up de tree to him, an' he helt de cheese crud in his hend, an' he says, 'I'll squeeze youah heart like dis flint stone.' An' de monkey cocked his eye, much to say, 'Ef you can squeeze a flint stone and mek de juice come outer it, you can squeeze me.' An' he never spoked, for a monkey's cunning, but down he went. An' de little bull-calf wuz fightin' all dese wild things on de groun', an' de little boy wuz clappin' his hands up de tree an' sayin': 'Go an, my little bull-calf! Well fit, my little bull-calf!' An' he mastered everyting barrin' de fiery dragin, an' de fiery dragin kilt de little bull-calf.

An' he wents an, an' saw a young lady, a king's darter staked down by de hair of her head. Dey wuz werry savage dat time of day, kings to deir darters, ef dey misbehavioured demselfs, an' she wuz put deah fur de fiery dragin to 'stry her.

An' he sat down wid her several hours, an' she says, 'Now, my deah little boy, my time is come when I'm a-goin' to be worried, an' you'll better go.' An' he says: 'No!' he says, 'I can master it, an' I won't go.' She begged an' prayed an him as ever she could to get him away, but he wouldn't go.

An' he could heah it comin' far enough, roarin' an' doin', an' dis dragin come spitting fire, wid a tongue like a gret speart, an' you could heah it roarin' fur milts, an' dis place wheah de king's darter wur staked down, was his beat wheah he used to come. An' when it comed, de little boy hit dis gut about his face tell he wuz dead, but de fiery dragin bited his front finger affer him.

Den de little boy cut de fiery dragin's tongue out, an' he says to de young lady: 'I've done all dat I can, I mus' leave you.' An' youah shuah she wuz sorry when he hed to leave her, an' she tied a dimant ring into his hair, an' said good-bye to him.

Now den, bime bye, de old king comed up to de werry place where his darter was staked by de hair of her head, 'mentin' an' doin', an' espectin' to see not a bit of his darter, but de prents of de place where she wuz. An' he wuz disprised, an' he says to his darter, 'How come you seft?' 'Why, deah wuz a little boy comed heah an' sef me, daddy.' Den he untied her, an' took'd her home to de palast, for youah shuah he wor glad, when his temper comed to him agin.

Well, he put it into all de papers to want to know who seft his gal, an' ef de right man comed he wur to marry her, an' have his kingdom an' all his destate. Well, deah wuz gentlemen comed fun all an' all parts of England, wid' deah front fingers cut aff an' all, an' all kinds of tongues, foreign tongues an' beastes tongues, an' wile animals' tongues. Dey cut all sorts of tongues out, an' dey went about shootin' tings a purpose, but dey never could find a dragin to shoot. Deah wuz gentlemen comin' every other day wid tongues an' dimant rings, but when dey showed deir tongues, it warn't de right one, an' dey got turn't aff.

An' dis little ragged boy comed up a time or two werry desolated like, an' she had an eye on him, an' she looked at dis boy, tell her father got werry angry an' turn't dis boy out. 'Daddy,' she says, 'I've got a knowledge to dat boy.'

Yoy may say, deah wuz all kinds of kings' sons comin' up showin' deah parcels, an' arter a time or two dis boy comed up agin dressed a bit better. An' de ole king says, 'I see you've got an eye on dis boy, an' ef it is to be him, it has to be him.' All de other *ryas* wuz fit to kill him, and dey says, 'Pooh! pooh! tun dat boy out; it can't be him.' But de ole king says, 'Now, my boy, let's see what you got.' Well, he showed de dimant ring, wid her name into it, an' de fiery dragin's tongue. *Dordi*! how dese gentlemen were mesmerized when he showed his 'thority, and de king tole him, 'You shall have my destate, an' marry my darter.'

An he got married to dis heah gal, an' got all de old king's destate, an' den de stepfather came an' wanted to own him, but de young king didn't know such a man.

38. Bobby Rag

Yeahs and yeahs an' double yeahs ago, deah wuz a nice young Gypsy gal playin' round an old oak tree. An' up comed a squire as she wur a-playin', an' he falled in love wid her, and asked her ef she'd go to his hall, an' marry him. An' she says: 'No, sir! you wouldn't have a pooah Gypsy gal like me.' But he meaned so, an' stoled her away an' married her.

Now, when he bring'd her home, his mother warn't 'greeable to let hisself down so low as to marry a Gypsy gal. So she says: 'You'll hev to go and 'stry her in de hundert mile wood, an' strip her star'-mother-naked, an' bring back her clothes and her heart and pluck wid you.'

And he took'd his hoss, and she jumped up behint him, and rid behint him into de wood. You'll be shuah it wor a wood! an ole-fashioned wood we know it should be, wid bears, an' eagles, an' sneks, an' wolfs into it. And when he took'd her in de wood he says: 'Now, I'll ha' to kill you here, an' strip you star'-mother-naked and tek back your clothes an' your heart an' pluck wid me, and show dem to my mammy.'

But she begged hard fur herself, an' she says: 'Deah's an eagle into dat wood, an' he's gat de same heart an' pluck as a Christ'n; take dat home an' show it to your mammy, an' I'll gin you my clothes as well.'

So he stript her clothes affer her, an' he kilt de eagle, and took'd his heart an' pluck home, an' showed it to his mammy, an' said as he'd kilt her.

And she hear'd him rode aff, an' she wents an, an' she wents an, an' she wents an, an' she crep' an' crep' an her poor dear hen's an' knees, tell she fun' a way troo de long wood. Youah shuah she'd have hard work to fin' a way troo it! an' long an' by last she got to de hedge anear de road, so as she'd hear any wan go by.

Now, in de marnin' deah wuz a young gentleman comed by an hossback, an' he couldn't get his hoss by for love nor money; an' she hed herself in under de hedge, fur she wur afrightened 'twor de same man come back to kill her agin, an' besides youah shuah she wor ashamed of bein' naked.

An' he calls out: 'Ef you're a ghost go 'way! but ef you're a livin' Christ'n, speak to me!' An' she med answer direc'ly: 'I'm as good a Christ'n as you are, but not in parable [apparel].' An' when he sin her, he pull't his deah, beautiful topcoat affer him, an' put it an her an' he says: 'Jump behint me.' An' she jumped behint him, an' he rid wi' her to his own gret hall. An' deah wuz no speakin' tell dey gat home. He knowed she wuz deah to be kilt, an' he galloped as hard as he could an his blood-hoss, tell he got to his own hall.

An' when he bring'd her in, dey wur all struck stunt to see a woman naked, wid her beautiful black hair hangin' down her back in long rinklets. Dey asked her what she wuz deah fur, an' she tell'd dem, an' she tell'd dem, an' youah shuah dey soon put clothes an her, an' when she wuz dressed up, deah warn't a lady in de land more han'some nor her, an' his folks wor in delight av her.

Now, dey says: 'We'll have a supper for goers an' comers an' all gentry to come at.' Youah shuah it should be a 'spensible supper an' no savation of money. And deah wuz to be tales tell'd an' songs sing'd, an' everywan dat didn't sing't a song had to tell't a tale; an' every door wuz bolted for fear any wan would mek a skip out.

An' it kem to pass to dis Gypsy gal to sing a song; an' de gentleman dat fun' her says: 'Now, my pretty Gypsy gal, tell a tale,' an' de gentleman dat wuz her husband knowed her, and didn't want her to tell a tale, and he says: 'Sing a song, my pretty Gypsy gal.'

An' she says: 'I won't sing a song, but I'll tell a tale.' An' she says:

> *Bobby rag! Bobby rag!*
> *Roun' de oak tree—*

'Pooh, pooh!' says her husband, 'dat tale won't do.' (Now, de ole mother an' de son, dey knowed what wuz comin' out.) 'Go an! my pretty Gypsy gal!' says de oder young gentleman. 'A werry nice tale indeed!'

So she goes on:

> *Bobby rag! Bobby rag!*
> *Roun' de oak tree.*
> *A Gypsy I wuz borned;*
> *A lady I wuz bred;*
> *Dey made me a coffin*
> *Afore I wuz dead.*

An' dats de rogue deah!' An' she tell't all de tale into de party, how he wur agoin' to kill her, an' tek her heart and pluck home. An' all de gentry took'd an' gibbeted him alive, both him an' his mother; an' dis young squire married her, an' med her a lady for life.

Ah! ef we could know her name, an' what breed she wur, what a beautiful ting dat would be, but de tale doan' say.

39. The Grey Castle

Oncet upon a time, and it wasn't in your time nor my time but it was in jolly good days, Jack left home. In his home he's left his poor old mother ahind on an owld box. And he was retermined to see life, 'cos he's never seen life afore.

He tramps along a dreary muddy road for miles and miles, and at long last he took a seat and reconsidered hisself, and he shook his head. 'Why did I, poor foolish boy, leave my home? What is mine own mother doing now 'ithout me? I wonder.'

He shook his head again, but he plucked up courage, brushed his coat and his cap, and started on tramp once more again. 'Now, Jack, dere's only yourself you got to talk to', says he, as he sighs his way along the dreary road. He begins to feel tired again so he rests his weary foot. De night is dark and bright stars above him, but he could not speak to de stars.

All at oncet dere stood a bright light in front of him, so he glared at it a-one-side, and with his brain and his heart wondered and plondered what was going to be at de end. 'Well, Jack old boy, cheer up, and now you must take a sleep.'

At long last de morn is comed and de birds begin deir bright singing, what lightened his heart a great deal. And the sun was shining so beautiful he could see de rocks and meadows clearly, and a large grey castle on a hill in front of him. 'Jack, my lad, you do not know what's afore you: dat castle may be your fortune.'

Jack sighed again, tired and dreary, hungry and dirsty, he gazed a-one-side at a grey owld farm-house. He ventured to open de gate and knocked at de farm door and asked de owld woman for a drink. De owld farmer-woman asked him quite snubbily as she handed him de tea: 'What is a young man like you doing about de country: have you no work?'

'No, dere isn't no work for Poor Jack', says he to dat owld
farmer-woman. 'Why?' she asks. 'Well,' says Jack, 'it's like a
good few of you farmers, you's a bit juberstitious of a man's
stealing summat. But bein' as you's made such a brag and a
boast 'bout it, we'll begin with you, missus. Is dere any work
for poor Jack from you?' 'Well, my man, only haarrd work!'

Jack laughed as she stood wid her coarse apron at de
door. 'Give me de chancet, missus, to see what I could do.'
'Well!' says she, quite sneery, 'what *can* you do?' 'Excuse
me,' says Jack, quite on de laughing side, pulling his cap off
so p'litely and brushing back his black hair, 'I'll give you an
offer of work now this instant minute. I'll chop dat big tree
for you, missus, into logs for your oven, for a little bite to eat.'
'Well,' says the woman, 'here's my chopper.' Jack smiles to
hisself and mutters: 'She's a hard piece of brick, is dat farmer-
woman.'

He worked away did Jack and, feeling very dreary, hungry
and dirsty, brought de wood to de door. 'Jack,' says she (quite
de thing now, you sees) 'you've done more work nor any one
of my men has done. Seat yourself down at dat table dis
instant minute', she says, 'and eat and drink of de best.'
'Now', thinks Jack to hisself, 'it's only de start of a dream for
you, my boy, it's only de first lesson. But somehow dese hard-
hearted manly women comes soft-hearted at de end.'

A'ter he'd done his food, he sits hisself down by de fireside
and has a little smoke and plonders very deeply about his
poor owld mother. And he starts to make amend very
smartly, and asks de missus could he have a wash. 'Ev
course,' says she, quite cheerful, 'it'll afresh you Jack.' And
out he goes with de bucket and soap (in a farm-house you
sees), and de farmer-woman hurries a'ter him and relivers
him de towel. 'Thank you kindly,' says Jack, 'you bin just
like a mother to me, but not ezackly like my poor owld
mammie: she used to cling to me and pray for me more nor
anybody in de world.'

Well, de owld woman fetches him a suit now, b'longing to
one of her sons, and begs him to stay de night. But all he
says is: 'How far is de next village from here, mum?' 'You
don't mean to say you will walk twenty miles to-night, Jack?
I want you to stay wid me and I'll give you good money and

good food. Do you know owt about ploughing?' 'No', he said quite stern to de owld woman, 'de best ploughing as ever I done, mum, is ploughing de hard road. So I'll stay no longer nor to-night, and mind you call me up six o'clock in de mornin'!'

De next morning is comed. He hears de gentle creak up de stairs, and up he jumps on de cheerful side. 'Well, Jack,' he says to hisself, 'you do look a smart, brisk lad now. And you'll soon make away for your dear hard road.' He enjoys his breakfast with de missus and tells her straight he must leave dis same morning. (He still has dat grey castle on his mind— he would do oncet he'd seen it.) 'Poor foolish Jack,' says she with a jeery laugh, 'I s'pose you's thinking of dat castle what you told me of. Dere's nowt dere for you, my boy, nowt what- sumdever! De very idea of you's going dere! poor foolish lad.' 'Well,' says Jack, 'I'm retermined to see life, and life I *will* see.'

So off he goes, carrying a little food wid him. He shuts de gate ahind him merrily, and starts a-laughing. 'Thank God', he says, 'I'm on de hard road again.' He starts a bit of hard walking, as he didn't think nothing of dat twenty miles. So he walked and he walked till he see'd de castle grinning at him. He sits hisself down and has a little smoke and he smiles to hisself. 'I'll soon make dat castle speak for itself too,' says he; 'it's bin on my brain long enough', he says.

Now he sees de lodge of dat castle, but he sees no light in dat lodge. But when he goes to de front door, he sees a bright light inside. So he smartens hisself and makes a 'tempt to knock at dat hard knocker. Now who comes out to him dere but an owld grey lady. She opens de door and gives him a little smile. 'Whatever do you want here, my boy?' says she. 'What a diff'rent voice she has', thinks Jack, 'towards dat hard brick!' And he laughs. 'I wants to know, mother,' he says, 'who lives up at dat owld grey castle.' 'You come in, my boy, and I'll 'tempt to 'splain to you. But you's very late: it's turned seven!' (It's in de night, you see, in dem country places.)

'Are you looking for work?' asked the old lady. 'Well, I bin here dese thirty years', she says 'and I've seen no men like you walking about de land.' (Poor hopes for Jack!) 'But dere's no harm in you's going up. Dere's only an owld gentleman dere', she says, 'and he's hard o' hearing.' (God help poor Jack!) 'Ah!' says Jack, 'never enter, never will.' (He was cheering hisself up.) 'When dere's a will, dere's a way. And I'm going up, mother,' he says. 'Good night, my boy, take care of you's self: you's got still two mile yet to go up to dat castle.'

Jack goes along through two big iron gates and makes his way up to de castle. (Thank God!) He goes over owld humpy, owld bumpy, owld stones, of course, but he doesn't care nowt for dese humpy, bumpy stones. He comed to de door of dat castle—dirty big lumps of lead on de door but a beautiful big knocker. He knocked on dat door.

Suddenly de door opened but he seen no one dere. He could not understand it. Dat door closened again. He knocked again. Suddently de door opened again. But still he seen no one dere.

So Jack stepped in den, cheekily. And what stood afore him? (Don't frighten! !) A little hairy owld man! 'What can I do for you, my strange man?' he says. 'I want work, Sir.' 'Ha! ha! ha!' says he, '*work* you want, is it? Come dis way, I'll show you WORK. Did anyone send you up here?' 'No', says Jack, quite cheerful. 'I must say you're a brave young man. Dere hasn't been anyone up here for thirty years. Well,' he said, 'I'll see about getting some WORK for you. When did you have something to eat last, my boy?' 'Oh! I don't feel hungry, thank you', says Jack. 'Well, I do', says de owld hairy man. 'Come dis way,' he say, 'you have not seen de Master yet.'

Jack begins to shiver. Jack begins to stare. And who should sit down at the great dinner table but a big Giant! Jack stared and stared. 'Well, my brave man', he says, 'come to look here for work, have you? Ha! ha! I'll give you WORK, if WORK it is you want!' Jack begins to miss de little hairy man.

'Sit down here', he says. (Dat's de Giant.) Jack begins to look around and shivers. He sees a 'normous plate afore him. 'You've to eat all dat!' (Poor Jack! he must have a big belly too.) 'Remember you haven't seen your master *yet*.' 'How many masters must I see?' thinks poor Jack to hisself. 'You'll want a place to sleep in, won't you?' 'Yes', says Jack.

164

'Come here, and I'll show you'—and dere stands his dear little hairy man again. Jack steps into the room and sees a 'normous big bed: 'Too big for me', he thinks to hisself. And who drops in dere but a bigger Giant nor what he'd seen afore, what would have been the mainstay of two Giants. 'You're not sleeping with me?' says Jack, and he begins to shiver again. 'No, my man, dat is your bed to you's self.' 'Well, I'll be very glad of a rest', says Jack. And he pulls his shoes off, does Jack, and he puts his head down on de pillow (thank God he did!) and he snores and snores till morning. (You wouldn't hardly know was it morning dere, it was always so dark—dat's why it's called de grey castle, you see!)

A ten pound knock comed to de door and shook de bed from under him. 'Come down for your breakfast, my man, come down!' Poor Jack goes down for his breakfast (certainly he would do, wouldn't you too?). And he sees de two Giants and the little s'rimp, de hairy man. 'Jack,' says de Giant, 'I want you to do some very hard work to-day. You'll have to go into de green room to-day. Dere stands a table before you, my boy, and you'll have to sleep dere for three nights, my boy, and unpick every single bit of rag dat's in dat great big rug.' 'I'll try my best, Sir', says poor Jack shivering again. The Giant went away and slammed the door on him.

Dere only stood two candles for his work. (God help him! he must have had good eyes too.) So he picked up de rug and started working. At last he begin to tremble: he partly knew dere was *somebody* about. And de 'normous big Giant with his glistening eyes came in. 'Well, Jack, have you found anything? Have you seen anything?' 'What d'you want me to see or find?' says Jack. 'Is dere anything in dis dark room to find or to see?' he says. 'Seek not for inflamation!' said de big Giant, 'but get on wid your work!' De door goes slam, wid a fast lock. (Poor Jack!)

Jack begins to work again, and suddenly he looks towards a big long chest what stood in de darkest corner. And he hears a whisper: 'Pull it from de middle, Jack, and your three days' job will soon be finished. But do not say dat you heard anything.'

De Giant comes in (dat Giant is a Devil, you know!) shining de room up wid his glittering eyes. 'You're doing your work wonnerful, Jack, but I'm not quite satisfied. You must have seen someone to help you do dat rug.' 'I don't know what you's talking about', says Jack. The Giant goes out de same old way with a slam of de door.

It suddenly struck Jack about de owld chest what stood in de corner. He stepped up to it and was 'tempted to undo de lock. (Go ahead, Jack!) De word was spoken: 'You can't undo dat lock. Look on de shelf, Jack, and look pretty sharp, and you'll find de key of de chest.' Jack looks sharp and finds de key.

He unlocks de chest and suddenly de lid opens, and he staggers back. He sees inside de glitter of a beautiful green dress and a figure wid a pale face: a lovely lady. Den she up and spoke to Jack afore she lays down again. 'Jack,' she says, 'I have been locked in dis chest for de last thirty years.' Jack is staggered. 'Are you a ghost?' he asks. 'No,' says she, 'I'm human like what you are, dere's still a bit of life in me. I'm in my wedding dress', she says. 'You are my brave man, Jack,' she says, 'and dose two Giants are 'chanted and dat little hairy man is my father. And now, Jack, I've told you my secret. So don't hesitate, Jack; close de chest, fasten de lock and say nothing'. By this time de whole rug is unpicked.

At last bum! bum, bum! de Giant is coming. 'Come in!' cries Jack. 'My word, you have worked dat cloth beautiful, Jack. You must have found something, or seen someone.' 'Dere's only one more thing, Jack,' he says, 'you've got to do for me: to go to dat pond outside de castle and find two diamond rings.' 'Well,' says Jack, very disheartened, 'it's impossible, Sir, to find two diamond rings.' The Giant glared at him quite furiously.

Poor Jack goes out to dis dirty black pond, and he plondered to hisself could he find dese two diamond rings. At long last he sees a beautiful white swan and Jack thinks to have a chat with dis swan. Suddenly it made up to him. And Jack got more frightened of de swan nor what he got of de Giants. 'Poor Jack,' says she, 'just follow me and I'll show you where are dose diamond rings.' Jack followed de swan up to de pond. 'Don't get disheartened, Jack, I've got dose diamond rings for you.' And de swan lifted up her bill and dere were de rings she'd picked up from de bottom of de pond. 'And now, Jack, go back to dat Giant and tell him you've seen no one, and give dose two rings into his own hands.'

Back goes Jack, quite cheerful, steps into de green room, goes up to de chest de first thing and opens de lid, and speaks gently to de lovely green lady. He shows her de diamond rings. 'Jack,' says she, 'my good lad, give dem to dat Brute, and do not return here again to me. You will find me somewhere else.'

Jack goes bravely from her, and steps up to de big Giant, quite cheeky. 'Here you are, you Brute!' he says. 'What! what! what!' says de Giant, 'dose same two diamond rings what caused a lot of bloodshed? Well!' he says to Jack (quite de thing now, you sees) 'you've fulfilled your work, you've beat me, Jack. And you've won de grey castle. You'll be "poor" Jack no longer! I must leave you for a minute. Go into de green room, Jack, and you shall have your reward.'

Poor Jack goes into de other room quite happy and proud. And a nice gentleman met him at de door. He was looking for de little hairy owld man, but he couldn't see him—only dis very nice gentleman to keep poor Jack company.

Suddenly he seed de castle all of a light-shine, what he'd never seed afore. De gentleman dances him into another great big room, and he could see de table laid out with chickens and ducks and all sorts of good things, and he was plondering where were de guests. And suddenly two beautiful young gentlemen appear, shining like de rising sun. He was looking for de two Giants, and lo and behold!—dese two young gentlemen.

Jack was quite excited and quite exhausted. Den who comes in a'ter, but a lovely lady in a pale green dress and a green veil. She comes up to Jack and says: 'Jack, my boy, you have brokened our 'chantment.' With dat, she throws back her green veil and stands afore him—the handsomest young lady in all de land.

Den dey all gathered together—de father, de two brothers and Jack and de lady—'ithout one enemy in de world. And Jack married de lovely lady. And so dey lived happy for ever more after.

SCOTTISH

*Recorded by Andrew McCormick
from Mary MacMillan*

---

40. The Enchanted Man

There were two brothers, and they were very handsome and gentlemanly in appearance, but they hadn't got very much money where they lived. One said to the other: 'We'll travel to such and such a castle, and we'll get good money there. You can be gardener, and I'll be coachman.' The other said that he was agreeable to go with him. 'I think it will be better for us to go.' So they packed their things and went off in the morning far further than I'll tell you or you'll tell me.

Night came on. They came to a wild forest. One said to the other: 'We are fatigued. The night is good. Let us have a night's rest.' They took some afreshments and fell into a slumber, and dreamed that they would come to a castle, get bed and victuals better than they had. One brother woke the other and said: 'We do wrong to wait here. We will go to this castle. It's an inn, but it's like a castle. We shall get rest there far better than we can have here.' They went away far further than I'll tell you or you'll tell me, and came to this inn.

'We'll go in. They'll do nothing to us.' In the brothers go. They look to the right and they look to the left, but see nobody. There is a great big table, tea dishes on it and food of all kinds, a beautiful fire with a teapot beside it. They made up their minds to help themselves, and sit down and get the best of afreshments. The teapot attends to them. They take their satisfaction. There is a candle and candlestick on the table. Up get this candle and candlestick and walk off the table.

'We'll see where they are going', said the brothers. So they followed them, and walked into a beautiful bedroom. The candle and candlestick sat down on a table. The brothers looked and saw a beautiful bed folded down. 'We shall have a good night's rest here', said the brothers. They got into the bed.

If the place was beautiful at night, it was more so in the morning, but still there was no person to be seen. As it had done the night before, the teapot got up and filled all the cups, and still nobody appeared. The brothers take their breakfast, and then resume their journey. They go far further than I'll tell you or you'll tell me till night comes on again.

They come to another castle larger and more beautiful than the last one. They walk round and round, but can find no entrance except by the hall door. 'We'll venture in.' In they go. Everything beautiful—handsome table, beautiful dishes. Everything shining and beautiful. 'We'll have some afreshments. Everything is good, and nobody is here to hinder us.' Up gets the teapot and fills the cups. It's a grand table—knives and forks and grand dishes set for a lot of folk. Still the brothers could see nobody, and every dish was emptying as soon as theirs. There was a candle and candlestick sitting on the table. Up get this candle and candlestick and walk off the table. 'We'll see where you go.' They follow and come into a bedroom. Down sit the candle and candlestick. 'We shall have a night's rest. There's nothing to hinder us.'

In the morning when they're going to rise here's a black lady, all black, only her face white. She never spoke until they had good afreshments. 'You were in my sister's house last night. You are in my house to-night. You'll be in another sister's to-morrow night. Tell her that you saw me, and that I spoke to you.' 'We'll do that, madam. And will it be a long distance?' 'Something like a hundred and fifty miles, but you will not be long in going that.'

The young gentlemen continue their journey. They go far further than I'll tell you or you'll tell me, and they push along, for night comes on and they want rest. They come to a third castle, and they go round and round, but the only entrance is by the front door. 'It's only death anyway; we'll venture in.' And if the second place was beautiful, the third was far more beautiful. The table was shining with white covers, six tea dishes and plates, and a great fire and every kind of grand foods. This is extra good. Here comes the teapot, fills out the six tea dishes. Still they could see nobody, and every dish was emptying as soon as theirs. 'This is something queer.' The candle and candlestick as before walk off the table. 'We'll see where you're going.' They follow the candle and candlestick and look and see a beautiful bed.

They have a night's rest, and in the morning here comes a black lady, and she is all black except the face and neck. Yet she never spoke until they got their breakfast. 'You were in my sister's house last night, and you are in mine to-night. You must now return home, and on your way you will stop at my sisters' houses, and the last house you enter you will go no further. You'll find your work. Turn back this morning. Go back to the second inn this night.'

They turn back, and when they come to the inn they go round again and can find no entrance, only by the front door. Something like a 'waff' goes through the house. Everything is beautiful. They have afreshments, and there are bottles of wine sitting all round the table. 'Maybe that's left to see what we'll do. We won't touch it. We have got good afreshment. We'll see about getting rest.' They follow the candle and candlestick as before, and walk into a bedroom. There's always a 'waff-waffing', but they can see nothing. They go to bed, and have a night's rest.

In the morning a young lady enters, white down to the breast. 'How did you rest last night? Did anything disturb you?' 'Nothing but a bad dream.' They dress and come down to breakfast. The table is more beautiful in the morning than it was the night before. 'You will be at my sister's house to-night, and that will be your destination. You can be a gardener, and you can be a coachman, but you have to break the enchantment.' 'We'll do that.'

They go on their journey far further than I'll tell you or you'll tell me to this other inn. They go round this place, but there's no entrance except by the front door. 'We will venture in.' What a beautiful table! Everything was beautiful and shining. There is a dreadful 'waff' going through the place, but no person is seen. They sit down to take their afreshment, and there is a bottle of wine at each corner of the table, but they don't touch the wine. When they are satisfied the candle and candlestick again walk off the table, and they follow. The candle and candlestick sit down on a table in a beautiful bedroom. They look and see a fine bed and go to rest.

In the morning a young lady appeared, white all over—a most beautiful young lady. 'How did you rest last night?' 'Pretty well, my lady.' 'Did nothing disturb you?' 'Nothing but a small dream.' 'I must say you are the noblest young gentlemen ever entered my realm. You shall be gardener, and you coachman. The horse you have to drive is enchanted, and there is only one rod you can use to break the enchantment. You must find that rod. My only brother was struck [by it] into this horse. There's only one place in this garden, one place in this orchard, where you are to "snod" the trees. You have to root some of them out. There are parts of this garden you are not to touch.' They agree to be the servants. They look at this and that through the house. Everything is beautiful. The coachman looks at the horse, then he looks at the horse's manger. He sees a bit of a small rod, white peeled. He looks at it. 'That'll be heavy enough to drive a good horse.' He gets his rod.

There are three sisters in each inn—nine altogether. This is their brother that's enchanted. The coachman gets orders to have the carriage ready to take the sisters for a drive. The nine sisters get into the carriage. 'What destination?' 'Such and such a destination, provided man and horse keep good.' 'My horse will keep good.'

They go about a mile, and he touches the horse with the rod for the first time. The moment he touches the horse he sees the appearance of a man's shoulder where he struck the horse. He pays no attention. About a mile further on he hits the horse again and a hand appears. He drives on. He hits the horse again for the third time. Another hand and shoulder come. He strikes again. This time the head and neck appear. And the ladies cannot conceive how he got this rod. But he is near the destination. He must hit the horse for every sister that is in the carriage—nine times. He strikes for the fifth time. He has almost the whole man together now. He has only two legs of the horse. Hits again—but one leg to go: it's the man that's pulling the machine now—till he hits the horse eight times and the horse falls down. He says: 'My ladies, I humbly beg your pardon. There's something wrong with the horse.' They were very much put about.

'Do not excite yourself, coachman. We will get out, and you can assist your horse.' One of the sisters comes up to the driver, and she drops something into his pocket. One after another comes and drops something into the driver's pocket. He was standing working and fixing about his horse, and he thought it was imagination. The eldest sister says: 'Put your hand into your right pocket, pull something out and scatter it over your horse.' He finds a stalk of corn, and throws it over the horse. 'Put your hand in your pocket', says another sister, 'and you'll find something.' He finds a head of wheat and throws it over the horse. The horse gives a kick and a cry. It is almost a human body now, but he throws and he throws till he has thrown all the nine bits of things. When he has scattered the last bit of stuff over the horse, it jumps up into a man. The enchantment is broken.

ANGLO-WELSH

*Recorded by Francis Hindes Groome
from John Roberts*

———————·———————

41. Jack and his Golden Snuff-Box

Once upon a time there was an old man and an old woman, and they had one son, and they lived in a great forest. And their son never saw any other people in his life, but he knew that there was some more people in the world besides his own father and mother, because he had lots of books, and he used to read every day about them. And when he read about some pretty young women, he used to go mad to see some of them. Till one day, when his father was out cutting wood, he told his mother that he wished to go away to look for his living in some other country, and to see some people besides them two. And he said, 'I see nothing at all here but great trees around me; and if I stay here, maybe I shall go mad before I see anything.'

The young man's father was out all this time, when the conversation was going on between him and his poor old mother.

The old woman begins by saying to her son before leaving, 'Well, well, my poor boy, if you want to go, it's better for you to go, and God be with you.' (The old woman thought for the best when she said that.) 'But stop a bit before you go. Which would you like best for me to make you—a little cake and to bless you, or a big cake and to curse you?'

'Dear! dear!' said he, 'make me a big cake. Maybe I shall be hungry on the road.'

The old woman made the big cake, and she went on top of the house, and she cursed him as far as she could see him.

He presently meets with his father, and the old man says to him, 'Where are you going, my poor boy?' When the son told the father the same tale as he told his mother, 'Well,' says his father, 'I'm sorry to see you going away, but if you've made your mind to go, it's better for you to go.'

The poor lad had not gone far, till his father called him back; when the old man drawed out of his pocket a golden snuff-box, and said to him: 'Here take this little box, and put it in your pocket, and be sure not to open it till you are near your death.'

And away went poor Jack upon his road, and walked till he was tired and hungry, for he had eaten all his cake upon the road; and by this time night was upon him, as he could hardly see his way before him. He could see some light a long way before him, and he made up to it, and found the back door and knocked at it, till one of the maidservants came and asked him what he wanted. He said that night was on him, and he wanted to get some place to sleep. The maidservant called him in to the fire, and gave him plenty to eat, good meat and bread and beer; and as he was eating his refreshments by the fire, there came the young lady to look at him. And she loved him well, and he loved her. And the young lady ran to tell her father, and said there was a pretty young man in the back kitchen. And immediately the gentleman came to him, and questioned him, and asked what work he could do. He said, the silly fellow, that he could do anything. (Jack meant that he could do any foolish bit of work, what would be wanted about the house.)

'Well,' says the gentleman to him, 'at eight o'clock in the morning I must have a great lake and some of the largest man-of-war vessels sailing before my mansion, and one of the largest vessels must fire a royal salute, and the last round break the leg of the bed where my young daughter is sleeping on. And if you don't do that, you will have to forfeit your life.'

'All right', said Jack. And away he went to his bed, and said his prayers quietly, and slept till it was near eight o'clock and he had hardly any time to think what he was to do, till all of a sudden he remembered about the little golden box that his father gave him. And he said to himself, 'Well, well, I never was so near death as I am now'; and then he felt in his pocket, and drew the little box out.

And when he opened it, there hopped out three little red men and asked Jack, 'What is your will with us?'

'Well,' said Jack, 'I want a great lake and some of the largest man-of-war vessels in the world before this mansion, and one of the largest vessels to fire a royal salute, and the last round to break one of the legs of the bed where this young lady is sleeping on.'

'All right,' said the little men; 'go to sleep.'

Jack had hardly time to bring the words out of his mouth, to tell the little men what to do, but what it struck eight o'clock, when bang, bang, went one of the largest man-of-war vessels; and it made Jack jump out of bed to look through the window. And I can assure you it was a wonderful sight for him to see, after being so long with his father and mother living in a wood.

By this time Jack dressed himself, and said his prayers, and came down laughing, because he was proud, he was, because the thing was done so well. The gentleman comes to him, and says to him, 'Well, my young man, I must say that you are very clever indeed. Come and have some breakfast.' And the gentleman tells him: 'Now there are two more things you have to do, and then you shall have my daughter in marriage.' Jack gets his breakfast, and has a good squint at the young lady, and also she at him.

(However, I must get on again with my dear little story.)

The other thing that the gentleman told him to do was to fell all the great trees for miles around by eight o'clock in the morning; and, to make my long story short, it was done, and it pleased the gentleman well. The gentleman said to him, 'The other thing you have to do' (and it was the last thing), 'you must get me a great castle standing on twelve golden pillars; and there must come regiments of soldiers, and go through their drill. At eight o'clock the commanding officer must say, "Shoulder up".' 'All right', said Jack. When the third and last morning came and the three great feats were finished, he had the young daughter in marriage.

But, oh dear! there is worse to come yet.

The gentleman now makes a large hunting party, and invites all the gentlemen around the country to it, and to see the castle as well. And by this time Jack has a beautiful horse and a scarlet suit to go with them. On that morning his valet, when putting Jack's clothes by, after changing them to go a-hunting, put his hand in one of Jack's waistcoat pockets and pulled out the little golden snuff-box, as poor Jack had left behind in a mistake. And that man opened the little box, and there hopped the three little red men out, and asked him what he wanted with them. 'Well,' said the valet to them, 'I want this castle to be moved from this place far and far across the sea.' 'All right,' said the little red men to him, 'do you wish to go with it?' 'Yes', said he. 'Well, get up', said they to him; and away they went, far and far over the great sea.

Now the grand hunting party comes back, and the castle upon the twelve golden pillars disappeared, to the great disappointment of those gentleman as did not see it before. That poor silly Jack is threatened by taking his beautiful young wife from him, for taking them in the way he did. But the gentleman is going to make a 'greement with him, and he is to have a twelvemonth and a day to look for it; and off he goes with a good horse and money in his pocket.

Now poor Jack goes in search of his missing castle, over hills, dales, valleys, and mountains, through woolly woods and sheepwalks, further than I can tell you to-night or ever intend to tell you. Until at last he comes up to the place where lives the King of all the little mice in the world. There was one of the little mice on sentry at the front gate going up to the palace, and did try to stop Jack from going in. He asked the little mouse, 'Where does the King live? I should like to see him.' This one sent another with him to show him the place; and when the King saw him, he called him in. And the King questioned him, and asked him where he was going that way. Well, Jack told him all the truth, that he had lost the great castle, and was going to look for it, and he had a whole twelve-month and a day to find it out. And Jack asked him whether he knew anything about it; and the King said, 'No, but I am the King of all the little mice in the world, and I will call them up in the morning, and maybe they have seen something of it.'

Then Jack got a good meal and a bed, and in the morning he and the King went on to the fields; and the King called all the mice together, and asked him whether they had seen the great beautiful castle standing on golden pillars. And all the little mice said, No, there was none of them had seen it. The old King said to him that he had two other brothers: 'One is the King of all the frogs; and my other brother, who is the oldest, he is the King of all the birds in the world. And if you go there, maybe they know something about it' [the missing castle]. The King said to him, 'Leave your horse here with me till you come back, and take one of my best horses under you, and give this cake to my brother; he will know then who you got it from. Mind and tell him I am well, and should like dearly to see him.'

And then the King and Jack shook hands together. And when Jack was going through the gates, the little mouse asked him should he go with him; and Jack said to him, 'No, I shall get myself into trouble with the King.'

And the little thing told him, 'It will be better for you to have me go with you; maybe I shall do some good to you sometime without you knowing it.' 'Jump up, then.' And the little mouse ran up the horse's leg, and made it dance; and Jack put the mouse in his pocket. Now Jack, after wishing good morning to the King, and pocketing the little mouse which was on sentry, trudged on his way. And such a long way he had to go, and this was his first day. At last he found the place; and there was one of the frogs on sentry, and gun upon his shoulder, and did try to hinder Jack not to go in. And when Jack said to him that he wanted to see the King, he allowed him to pass; and Jack made up to the door. The King came out, and asked him his business; and Jack told him all from beginning to ending. 'Well, well, come in.'

He gets good entertainment that night; and in the morning the King made a curious sound, and collected all the frogs in the world. And he asked them, did they know or see anything of a castle that stood upon twelve golden pillars. And they all made a curious sound, *Kro-kro, kro-kro*, and said 'No'.

Jack had to take another horse, and a cake to his brother which is the King of all the fowls of the air. And as Jack was going through the gates, the little frog which was on sentry asked John should he go with him. Jack refused him for a bit; but at last he told him to jump up, and Jack put him in his other waistcoat pocket. And away he went again on his great long journey; it was three times as long this time as it was the first day; however, he found the place, and there was a fine bird on sentry. And Jack passed him, and he never said a word to him. And he talked with the King, and told him everything, all about the castle. 'Well,' said the King to him, 'you shall know in the morning from my birds whether they know anything or not.'

Jack put up his horse in the stable, and then went to bed, after having something to eat. And when he got up in the morning the King and he went on to some fields, and there the King made some funny noise, and there came all the fowls that were in all the world. And the King asked them, Did they see the fine castle? and all the birds answered 'No'. 'Well,' said the King, 'where is the great bird?'

They had to wait then, for a long time, for the eagle to make his appearance, when at last he came all in a perspiration, after sending two little birds high up in the sky to whistle on him to make all haste he possibly could. The King asked the great bird, Did he see the great castle? And the bird said, 'Yes, I came from there where it now is.' 'Well,' says the King, 'this young gentleman has lost it, and you must go with him back to it. But stop till you get a bit of something to eat first.'

They killed a thief, and sent the best part of him to feed the eagle on his journey over the seas, and had to carry Jack on his back. Now, when they came in sight of the castle, they did not know what to do to get the little golden box. Well, the little mouse said to him: 'Leave me down, and I will get the little box for you.' So the mouse stole himself in the castle, and had a hold of the box; and when he was coming down the stairs, fell it down, and very near being caught. He came running out with it, laughing his best.

'Have you got it?' Jack said to him. 'He said, 'Yes'; and off they went back again, and left the castle behind. As they were all of them (Jack, mouse, frog and eagle) passing over the great sea, they fell to quarrelling about which it was that got the little box, till down it slipped into the water. (It was by them looking at it, and handing it from one hand to the other, that they dropped the little box in the bottom of the sea.)

'Well, well,' said the frog, 'I knew as I would have to do something, so you had better let me go down into the water.' And they let him go, and he was down for three days and three nights; and up he comes, and shows his nose and little mouth out of the water. And all of them asked him, 'Did he get it?' and he told them, 'No'. 'Well, what are you doing there, then?' 'Nothing at all,' he said; 'only I want my full breath.' And the poor little frog went down the second time, and he was down for a day and a night, and up he brings it.

And away they did go, after being there four days and nights; and, after a long tug over seas and mountains, arrive at the old King's palace, who is the master of all the birds in the world. And the King is very proud to see them, and has a hearty welcome and a long conversation. Jack opens the little box, and told the little men to go back and to bring the castle here to them. 'And all of you make as much haste back again as you possibly can.'

The three little men went off; and when they came near the castle, they were afraid to go to it, till the gentleman and the lady and all the servants were gone out to some dance. And there was no one left behind there, only the cook and another maid with her. And it happened to be that a poor Gypsy woman, knowing that the family was going from home, made her way to the castle to try to tell the cook's fortune for a bit of victuals, was there at the time. And the little red men asked her: Which would she rather—go or stop behind? And she said, 'I will go with you.'

And they told her to run upstairs quick. She was no sooner up and in one of the drawing-rooms than there comes just in sight the gentleman and the lady and all the servants. But it was too late. Off they went with the castle at full speed, and the Gypsy woman laughing at them through the window, making motion for them to stop, but all to no purpose. They were nine days on their journey, in which they did try to keep the Sunday holy, by one of the little men turned to be priest, the other the clerk, and third presided at the organ, and the three women were the singers (cook, housemaid and Gypsy woman), as they had a grand chapel in the castle already. Very remarkable, there was a discord made in the music, and one of the little men ran up one of the organ-pipes to see where the bad sound came from, when he found out that it only happened to be that the three women were laughing at the little red man stretching his legs full length on the bass pipes, also his two arms the same time, with his little red nightcap, what he never forgot to wear, and what they never witnessed before, could not help calling forth some good merriment while on the face of the deep. And, poor things! through them not going on with what they begun with, they very near came to danger, as the castle was once very near sinking in the middle of the sea.

At length, after merry journey, they come again to Jack and the King. The King was quite struck with the sight of the castle; and going up the golden stairs, wishing to see the inside, when the first one that attracted his attention was the poor Gypsy woman. And he said to her, 'How are you, sister?' She said to him, 'I am very well. How are you?'

'Quite well', said he to her; 'come into my place, to have a talk with you, and see who you are, and who your people are.'

The old Gypsy woman told him that some of her people were some of them from the Lovells, Stanleys, Lees, and I don't know all their names. The King and Jack was very much pleased with the Gypsy woman's conversation, but poor Jack's time was drawing to a close of a twelvemonth and a day. And he, wishing to go home to his young wife, gave orders to the three little men to get ready by the next morning at eight o'clock to be off to the next brother, and to stop there for one night; also to proceed from there to the last or the youngest brother, the master of all the mice in the world, in such place where the castle shall be left under his care until it's sent for. Jack takes a farewell of the King, and thanks him very much for his hospitality, and tells him not to be surprised when he shall meet him again in some other country.

Away went Jack and his castle again, and stopped one night in that place; and away they went again to the third place, and there left the castle under his care. As Jack had to leave the castle behind, he had to take his own horse, which he left there when he first started. The King liked the Gypsy woman well, and told her he would like if she would stay there with him; and the Gypsy woman did stay with him until she was sent for by Jack.

Now poor Jack leaves his castle behind and faces towards home; and after having so much merriment with the three brothers every night, Jack became sleepy on horseback, and would have lost the road if it was not for the little men a-guiding him. At last he arrives, weary and tired, and they did not seem to receive him with any kindness whatever, because he did not find the stolen castle. And to make it worse, he was disappointed in not seeing his young and beautiful wife to come and meet him, through being hindered by her parents. But that did not last long. Jack put full power on. Jack despatched the little men off to bring the castle from there, and they soon got there; and the first one they seen outside gather sticks to put on the fire was the poor Gypsy woman. And they did whistle to her, when she turned around smartly and said to them, '*Dordi! dordi!* how are you, comrades? where do you come from, and where are you going?' 'Well, to tell the truth, we are sent to take this castle from here. Do you wish to stop here or to come with us?' 'I would like better to go with you than to stay here.' 'Well, come on, my poor sister.'

Jack shook hands with the King, and returned many thanks for his kingly kindness. When, all of a sudden, the King, seeing the Gypsy woman, which he fell in so much fancy with, and whom he so much liked, was going to detain the castle until such time he could get her out. But Jack, perceiving his intentions, and wanting the Gypsy woman himself for a nurse, instructed the little men to spur up and speed on. And off they went, and were not long before they reached their journey's end, when out comes the young wife to meet him with a fine lump of a young son.

Now, to make my long story short, Jack, after completing what he did, and to make a finish for the poor broken-hearted Gypsy woman, he has the loan of one of his father-in-law's largest man-of-wars, which is laying by anchor, and sends the three little men in search of her kinsfolk, so as they may be found, and to bring them to her. After long searching they are found, and brought back, to the great joy of the woman and delight of his wife's people-in-law, for after a bit they became very fond of each other. When they came on land, Jack's people allowed them to camp on their ground near a beautiful river; and the gentlemen and ladies used to go and see for them every day. Jack and his wife had many children, and had some of the Gypsy girls for nurses; and the little children were almost half Gypsies, for the girls continually learning them our language. And the gentleman and the lady were delighted with them. And the last time I was there I played my harp for them, and got to go again.

Recorded by John Sampson from Cornelius Price

42. Ashypelt

Once there was an old man and an old 'ooman livin' in the Forest o' Dean. They 'ad twelve sons, and there was one son called Ashypelt. He was the youngest son, and they didn't never think but little of Ashypelt, as 'ee was allus used to be i' the esshole under the fire, an' the brothers used to spit on 'im and laugh at 'im an' make fun of 'im an' that. He never spoke, didn't Ashypelt, nor hear nuthin'. These eleven brothers—they was nearly allus felling timber and that—used to go, they used to go off tel Saturdays for a week. They used to do that very reglar, and were bringing a lot of money in for the old man and the old 'ooman.

So the old 'ooman sez one day, 'Well, John, I sez, I think you an' me 'as got enough money now to live on which will keep we all the days of our life. An' we'll tell 'em to-night'— it was on a Saturday, an' they was comin' home again, they was comin' home with all the week's wages—'we'll say to 'em as the pressgang 'as been after 'em, as they've got to 'ear as we've got eleven very fine sons, and they wants to make soldiers of 'em. So I'll begin a-cryin' when they comes 'ere to-night, and I'll say to 'em, "O my very dear sons, the pressgang's been after yous 'ere to-day. They want yous to go for soldiers, an' the best you can do, my dear children" '— the old 'ooman was cryin' very much, makin' herself so— ' "is to go to sleep in the barn." An' we'll put 'em to sleep in the barn, an' give 'em their week's victuals with 'em' (what they used to take reglar), sez the old 'ooman to the old man. 'We can soon put Ashypelt out o' the road.' (He was listening all the time, the poor Ashypelt, listenin' wot the old 'ooman was sayin'.) 'Soon as we've put the eleven sons in the barn we'll set fire to 'em about twelve o'clock and burn 'em: that's the best way to take it out of 'em. We'll burn 'em', she sez.

Poor Ashypelt gets up out o' the esshole—this was about the hour of eleven: they was sittin' up till twelve to set the barn afire. He goes up to the barn, an' 'ee throws 'is brothers up one after another neck and crop—an' they was goin' to kill 'im—an' their week's victuals.

'Oo are you?' they sez.

'I am your brother Ashypelt', he sez, 'I am your brother Ashypelt.'

So one looks at 'im, an' another looks at 'im, to find a certain mark as they know to him. They went to kill poor Ashypelt for throwing them up.

He sez, 'My father and mother is goin' to set you afire, all the lot o' you, that's the reason they put you in the barn. An' come with me up on that back edge, an' you'll see the barn goin' afire directly', sez Ashypelt.

They sat on this high edge tel twelve o'clock come, an' they was lookin' out, an' they seen the old 'ooman an' the old man go with a lantern, an' puttin' a light to the barn an' all the straw what was in it. So they thanked Ashypelt very much for savin' their lives, but they didn't injure their father or mother; but they all started to go on the road together. They comes to twelve cross-roads; an' poor Ashypelt, never bein' out o' the esshole before, 'ee took very sleepy, through bein' a very 'ot day.

So one brother sez to the other, 'We'll all take a road to ourselves. Each one will take a road, an' in twelve months an' a day we'll all meet 'ere agen.'

So poor Ashypelt the sun overcame 'im, an' 'im never bein' out o' the esshole, 'ee fell asleep; an' each brother left

183

a mark on the road which way they went, for 'im to go 'is road to 'imself. When poor Ashypelt wakened up, 'ee began lookin' round 'im an' rubbin' 'is eyes. They left 'im a very nasty old lane to go up, an old nasty lane with the mud up to your knees. Poor Ashypelt bein' very weak, he got fast several times goin' up this old lane, an' tumbled down in the mud; an' the 'edges was growed very high with 'em so meetin' together; and the briers was scratching poor Ashypelt's eyes very near out, as 'ee was goin' up this old lane. 'Ee travels on, over high dales an' lofty mountains, where the cock never crowed and the divel never sounded 'is bugle horn. (It'll last tel to-morrow night, but I don't mean to half tell you so long.) But poor Ashypelt got benighted up this old lane. 'Ee used to fall asleep, bein' summer-time, an' very early in the mornin' come daylight 'ee wakens up, an' 'ee kept on the same old lane all the way he was goin'. 'Ee travels on tel 'ee comes to a castle an' a new 'ouse, where there was a man, an' 'ee axed this man could 'ee give 'im a job.

'Ee sez, 'Yes, Ashypelt, I can give you a job', 'ee sez. 'Ee sez, 'Wot can you do?' Ashypelt sez, 'I can do everythink as you try to put me to.' 'Well, Ashypelt,' 'ee sez, 'I'll give you fifty pounds to sleep into the castle all night, an' a good suit o' clo'es.' 'Oh! yes,' 'ee sez; 'I'll sleep there', 'ee sed.

So 'ee sez to Ashypelt, 'ee sez, 'You shall have a good bag o' nuts to crack an' plenty o' 'bacca to smoke, an' a good fire to sit by', 'ee sez. But 'ee allowed him no can o' beer to drink, plenty o' water, so as he wouldn't get trussicated. An' 'appen about eleven o'clock that night 'ee sez, 'Now Ashypelt, it is about the time you've got to come in along o' me.'

So 'ee takes Ashypelt with 'im about eleven o'clock to this castle. 'Ee opens the door, an' 'ee sez, 'There you are, go an' take your seat, an' sit down.' 'Ee sez, 'Here is your bag o' nuts, an' plenty o' 'bacca to smoke.'

So just now Ashypelt was sittin' down, an' just about the hour o' twelve 'ee could 'ear a lot o' noise about the room. 'Ee looks around behind 'im at the door, an' 'ee sees a man naked. So 'ee sez, 'Come up to the fire an' warm you. You looks very cold.' It was a sperrit, you see. 'Ee wouldn't come up to the fire, so Ashypelt went an' fetched 'im. Ashypelt sez, 'Will you 'ave a smoke?' 'ee sez, an' 'ee takes an' 'ee fills 'im a new pipe. 'Ee sez, 'Will you crack some nuts?' So 'ee smoked all poor Ashypelt's 'bacca, an' cracked all 'is nuts, an' poor Ashypelt 'ad none. But 'ee sez, 'You are a very greedy fellow indeed, I must say,' 'ee sed, 'after a man bringing you up to warm you at the fire, an' taking everything off 'im.'

Just about the hour o' two o'clock away goes this man from 'im. So therefore Ashypelt sits contented down afore the fire to hisself.

So next mornin' the master sez to 'im at the hour o' six o'clock, 'Are you alive, Ashypelt?' 'Oh! yes,' 'ee sez to 'im, 'I am alive, sir. An' there came a very rude man 'ere last night, an' took all my 'bacca, an' cracked all my nuts off me', 'ee sez, 'for the kindness I done for 'im. 'Ee was naked, an' I axed 'im to 'ave a warm.'

'Well,' 'ee sez to Ashypelt, 'come along an' 'ave some breakfast, Ashpelt.' An' 'ee takes 'im to the new 'ouse from the castle, to 'ave some breakfast. 'Would you wish to stop another night, Ashypelt?' 'ee sez, 'an' I'll give you another fifty pounds.' 'Oh! yes,' sez Ashypelt, 'im never seein' anythin', an' never knowin' wot sperrits or ghostses was, 'im bein' allus in the esshole.

So all day Ashypelt went up an' down the garden, an' learnin' 'ow to dig in the garden an' one thing or another, tel eleven o'clock came again the next night. 'Well, come, Ashypelt, my lad,' 'ee sed, 'it's time for you to go back to your room agen now.'

So the next night 'ee gave 'im very near 'alf a pound o' 'bacca to smoke an' a bigger bag o' nuts. So about the hour o' twelve o'clock 'ee turns round to the door again, an' there was five or six of these ghostses came in to 'im this time an' sperrits. So there was one stood up in the corner in 'is skeleton. There was five more runnin' up and down the room pitity-pat, pitity-pat. 'Come up to the fire', Ashypelt sez, 'an' warm yous. Yous look very cold all runnin' about naked', 'ee sed. 'Ee sez, 'There's some 'bacca there an' some pipes. 'Ave a smoke apiece.'

So this poor fellow stood up in the corner. 'You come 'ere,' sed Ashypelt; 'you looks very cold, you're nuthin' but bones.' But 'ee gave Ashypelt no answer. So Ashypelt come up to

185

'im, to pull 'im out up to the fire, an' 'ee 'appened to give 'im a bit of a touch round the neck—somewhere under the jaw, I think it was—as 'ee wouldn't come for 'im. This fellow tumbled all into pieces, in small bits o' pieces about 'alf an inch, tumbled all into pieces when Ashypelt 'it 'im.

'Now, Ashypelt,' sez one of 'em, 'if you don't put that fellow up agen as you fun' 'im, we'll revour you alive.' Poor Ashypelt got fixing one little bone on top of another, an' one little bone on top of another, but 'ee got tumblin' them down as quick as 'ee was fixing them very near. Well, 'ee fixed an' fixed at last tel it come very near one o'clock that 'ee was bein' with 'im, but 'ee got 'em together agen. So away they all goes just about two o'clock an' leaves 'im; an' when 'ee come to look for the 'bacca, every morsel 'ad gone, 'ee never 'ad one pipeful.

'Well,' 'ee sez, 'they're a greedy lot o' fellows, them is', 'ee sez. 'They served me worse agen to-night', 'ee sez. So 'ee comes an' sits 'imself down completely by 'is own fire agen.

Next morning at the hour o' six o'clock the master comes for 'im agen. 'Are you alive, Ashypelt?' 'ee sez. 'Oh! yes,' 'ee sez, 'I'm alive.' He sez, 'Did you 'ear anythin' last night?' 'Yes,' sez Ashypelt, 'there come a lot o' greedy fellows 'ere, an' smoked all my 'bacca an' cracked all my nuts off me.'

So 'ee sez, 'Come on down, Ashypelt, an' 'ave your breakfast.' 'Ee takes 'im to the new 'ouse to 'ave 'is breakfast. But after 'ee'd 'ad 'is breakfast, 'Now, Ashypelt,' 'ee sez, 'I will give you another fifty to stop another night.' Well, poor Ashypelt, never 'avin' no money, 'ee sed, Yes, 'ee would do it. Well, 'ee took 'im, as usual, up an' down the garden agen next day with 'im, taking 'im up an' down the garden tel eleven o'clock come the next night.

'So now, Ashypelt, my boy, it's time for me to take you up to your room', 'ee sez. 'I'll give you a little extra 'bacca to-night. I'll give you a pound, an' a bigger bag o' nuts— altogether it might be a gohanna [guano] bag o' nuts—an' a pound o' 'bacca.' So 'ee fastened 'em into the room before Ashypelt comes, an' 'ee leaves 'im sitting down comfortable to 'isself 'avin' a bit o' a smoke o' 'is 'bacca. But 'ee 'eard one o' the terriblest noises 'ee ever 'eard in 'is life shoutin' blue wilful murders, but 'ee couldn't see nuthin'. This was at the

hour o' twelve. Bangin' one of 'is doors wide open, in comes
a man to 'im with 'is throat cut from 'ere to there. Ashypelt
axed 'im to come an' 'ave a pipe o' 'bacca, and to 'ave a
warm. Well, poor Ashypelt never seein' nuthin', 'ee wasn't
frightened a bit.

So the man sez to 'im, 'Now, Ashypelt, my boy, I see you
are not frightened. Come with me, an' I'll show you where I
lies. My brother 'as killed me—it's my brother what gives
you this money to stop 'ere. You come with me, Ashypelt,
down these steps. He took 'im down steps, down steps, down
steps. Ashypelt axed 'im 'ow much further 'ee 'ad to go, an'
it 'ad been very dark goin' down these steps. Ashypelt couldn't
see 'is way, but when 'ee got to the bottom there was a very
fine light.

'Now, Ashypelt,' 'ee sez, 'come with me', 'ee sez. 'I'm that
man as you struck ir the room an' knocked all to pieces. Now,
Ashypelt, I'll make you a gentleman for life if you'll do one
thing for me. Come along o' me', 'ee sez to Ashypelt. Then
'ee sez, 'Lift up that flag', 'ee sez. 'No, sir,' sez Ashypelt, 'I
can't lift it up', 'ee sez to 'im; 'but lift it you.' 'Put your 'and
down to it, an' try to lift it up', 'ee sed. Ashypelt done what
'ee told 'im, puttin' 'is 'and down to lift the flag, an' he draws
the flag up. What was under that but a big pot o' gold spade-
ace guineas an' that.

So 'ee sez, 'Come along o' me, Ashypelt,' 'ee sez, 'on
further', 'ee sez. 'Ee sez, 'Rise that flag up, Ashypelt.' Ashypelt
doin' so, 'ee told 'im to rise one flag up, 'ee sez, 'Rise the
other one, Ashypelt, next to it.' Ashypelt rises the other one,
an' there this 'ere skeleton was lyin' in the coffin. That's
where 'ee was buried; 'is brother buried 'im there into that
coffin. This was the older brother tel what the one was that
was alive, that was dead. But they got fallin' out which would
'ave the castle. The next brother killed the old one, an'
buried 'im there.

'Now, Ashypelt,' sez this man with his throat cut from 'ere
to there, 'I want you to do me a favourite, an' ', 'ee sez,
'you'll never be troubled no more. You can sleep in that
room all your lifetime,' 'ee sez, 'nuthin' will ever trouble you
no more. Now, in the mornin', 'ee sez, 'when my brother
comes for you, 'ee'll ax you what sort o' night's rest you 'ad.

So you say, "All right, only they smoked all my 'bacca an' cracked all my nuts agen." An' the first town you get to, Ashypelt, an' you leaves here, you make a report as 'ee's killed 'is own brother; an' when they calls for witnesses, Ashypelt, I'll repear into the hall with my throat cut from 'ere to there. You can come back, Ashypelt, an' take the castle, 'cause there's nobody takes the castle barrin' me an' my brother.'

So Ashypelt goes to the next town as 'ee could meet with, an' 'ee goes an' makes a 'larm to a magistrate; an' the magistrate sent some pleecemen with 'im, back to fetch this gentleman, an' Ashypelt goes with 'em. 'Hello!' sez 'ee to Ashypelt, 'what brings you back 'ere?' 'ee sed. So the pleeceman got close to this man. 'For you', 'ee sez, an' catches 'olt of 'im. 'They are come back for you, for killin' yourn brother', takin' 'im off back to the town agen, an' Ashypelt along with 'im, takin' 'im an' tryin' 'im. When they were tryin' 'im, at the hour o' twelve the magistrate cries out for witnesses, an' the man repears with 'is throat cut from 'ere to there, just as they cried out for witnesses. 'Is brother got life—twenty years; an' 'ee died shortly after 'ee got life. 'Ee broke 'is 'eart.

Well, Ashypelt goes back to the castle an' lives there, an' got a servant or two with 'im into the castle. One day 'ee bethought 'isself about 'is brothers where 'ee 'ad to meet them. 'Ee gets a pair of 'orses and a carriage, an' 'ee buys eleven suits o' clo'es, thinkin' upon 'is poor brothers. So 'ee drives ahead until 'ee comes to these twelve roads, where 'ee 'ad to meet 'em twelve months an' a day. So 'ee was drivin' up to these 'ere twelve roads, an' there they was all lyin' down.

'Hello! my men,' 'ee sez, 'what are you men all lyin' down for?' (Ashypelt bein' dressed up, lookin' gentleman, they didn't know 'im.) 'We're waitin' for a brother of ours by the name o' Ashypelt,' they sed. 'Would you know 'im if you would see 'im?' 'ee sed. 'Oh! yes, we would know 'im very well. Twelve months an' a day we 'ad to meet on these roads.' So 'ee sez to 'em, 'I'm your brother Ashypelt,' 'ee sed to the one. So they looks at 'im. 'If you're our brother Ashypelt, show your arm; you 'ave a mark on it what we know to.' So they looks at this mark. 'Oh! it is my brother Ashypelt', they sez, blessin' 'im an' kissin' 'im an' slobberin', an' so on.

So 'ee gives 'em a suit o' clo'es apiece, these eleven brothers, to put on. 'Now,' 'ee sez, 'I think we'll go back an' see the old 'ooman an' the old man, how they are gettin' on, from 'ere,' sez Ashypelt to 'is brothers. 'An' when we get nigh 'ome, you eleven brothers stop behind, an' I'll drive up to the little farm, an' ax the old lady what came of her eleven sons what she 'ad.'

So poor Ashypelt drives up to the 'ouse. 'Hello! my old lady,' 'ee sez, 'what's come of all the eleven sons as you 'ad?' 'Oh!' sez 'er, 'they all went off for soldiers.' So 'ee calls 'is eleven brothers up, an' 'ee sez, 'Didn't you try to burn my eleven brothers in that barn', 'ee sez, 'when you set the barn alight, an' told 'em as the pressgang o' soldiers was after 'em?' So she sez, 'No—true—no', she sed.

I tell you, sir, they give me a shilling for telling you that lie.

43. Jack and his Master

There was a wagoner at a farm and a dairy-maid, an' they got coortin' together. And in length of time this girl come that way by him. An' the master gid him a little 'ouse what was empty on the farm to live in, them bein' two good sarvints, an' the first child 'is name was Jack. In length of time the father died an' left this child to his mother.

This boy tuk to smokin' when 'ee was about twelve year old, an' 'ee got to robbin' the master's plow-socks to take 'em to the blacksmith's to sell 'em to rise bacca. And one day 'ee was prowlin' about an' 'ee meets the master's chain-harrow on the field, an' 'ee takes that to the blacksmith's and sells it.

Now the master was goin' down to the blacksmith's one day, 'avin' some business, an' 'ee 'appened to see 'is chain-harrow. ' 'Oo did you get this off?' 'ee sez. 'Off Jack', 'ee sez. 'Well, well!' 'ee sez, 'this boy'll ruin me afore long; he robs everythin' 'ee can lay 'is 'ands on.'

He goes back to the 'ouse, an' 'ee sez to the lad's mother: 'Either you or 'im'll 'ave to lave from 'ere, or your boy'll ruin me.' An' the poor mother began to cry, an' Jack was off the same time prowlin'. Jack comes back that night, an' 'is mother sez: 'Oh, Jack, my lad, you've done a very bad thing for we. Either you or me's got to lave the place.' 'Never mind, mother', sez Jack, 'I'll go.'

Poor Jack travels on, an' 'ee goes miles that night, till 'ee got benighted. He could see a light a distance off from 'im in the dark. So 'ee makes off for this light, an' when 'ee gets there, what was there but a big gentleman's hall? Who was standin' outside but the gentleman?

'Hello! my boy,' 'ee sez, 'where are you off to?' 'Ee sez: 'A-robbin' I'm goin', sir.' 'Ee sez: 'Take time a bit, my boy. I've eleven robbers in there myself now.' 'Oh, sir, I can't take time,' 'ee sez, 'I'm too hungry and footsore from travellin'; I must get in somewheres', 'ee sez, 'to find somethin' to ate.'

'Ee pulls a little pane out of the dairy winder, an' gets in through the winder. When 'ee gets inside 'ee finds a hard crus' of cheese and an empty candlestick. An' 'ee was gnawing at 'is crus' of cheese when one of the robbers comes into the pantry to 'im. An' 'ee works the trigger of the candlestick up and down displayin' it like a pistol, an' 'ee sez: 'Deliver your money or your life.' An' the robber 'ands 'im eleven pounds. They all comes out now, these eleven robbers, an' they was deliverin' the money up to the master, wot they got. An' this last one wot come out, 'ee sez to 'im, 'Where's yourn?' 'I've got none', 'ee sez. 'I 'ad eleven pounds tuk off me, and if I didn't give it up I should 'ave 'ad my brains blown off.'

Now the master sez to the men: 'Surround the 'ouse', 'ee sez, 'and watch which way 'ee comes out. Don't you 'urt 'im or 'arm 'im not till you brings 'im to me.' In happen 'ee came out where the master stood, the same way as 'ee went in.

So 'Hello, my boy,' 'ee sez, ' 'ow did you get on?' 'Well, sir,' 'ee sez, 'there was someone inside there, and I 'ad eleven pounds off 'im.' 'Ee sed: 'Would you like to come for apprentice for a robber, my boy, and I'll give you so much a week?' 'Yes, sir,' 'ee sez, 'I don't mind.'

So 'ee was with them for about six months, an' 'ee got a

cleverer robber than wot the master 'isself was. 'Ee 'ad a bit of money by 'im, an' 'ee thought 'ee'd make 'is way back to 'is mother to see 'ow she was gettin' on.

As 'ee was goin' back near home 'ee meets this farmer on the road. 'Hello, Jack, my lad,' 'ee sez, 'where 'ave you bin?' 'I've bin prentice to a robber', 'ee sez. 'Prentice to a robber, my lad;' 'ee sez, 'you was big enough robber when you was 'ere afore. Well, Jack,' 'ee sez, 'I'll try if you can rob.' 'Ee sez, 'My man's goin' to sich a place to-morrow for a ship [sheep], and,' 'ee sez, 'if you can't take that ship off 'im without 'is seein' you, I shall be-behead you.'

Jack gets up the next morning, an' 'ee jus' 'as a look wot sort of man was goin' for the ship. And all Jack looked at was 'is feet, an' the man 'ad a very bad pair of boots on. So Jack sez, 'I'll soon do you', 'ee sez, an' 'ee goes to the shop an' 'ee buys a pair of eights.

So Jack puts these shoes under 'is arm, and makes 'is way on the road to meet this man, by a wood. So Jack listens for 'im at the end of this wood, an' 'ee 'ears 'im comin'. 'Ee was comin', goin' 'Yoop, yooee!' to the ship, an' the ship was goin' 'Baaaa'. And Jack sez: ' 'Ee's comin', now's my time.' So as 'ee was comin' along, Jack drops a new shoe in the road, and walks on in front of 'im. The man picks up this new shoe, an' tries it on 'is foot. 'Eh, sirree!' 'ee sez, 'shouldn't I look well if I 'ad t'other 'un, an' I'll lave it where I fund it, 'cause if I was to go 'ome with a new shoe and an old 'un, how the master would laugh at me.'

In happen 'ee goes on the road for four or five hundred yards further, an' 'ee fund t'other in the road. 'Eh, sirree!' 'ee sez, 'wot a fool I must be to throw the t'other 'un in the road, now I've fund this 'un. Well,' 'ee sez, 'it wouldn't take me not long to go back for the t'other, if I tie the ship to the hedge; and shan't I look grand goin' 'ome to the master with a new pair of boots on?' He goes back for the t'other.

So while 'ee was away, Jack goes an' collars the ship, and away 'ee goes with it! He takes it 'ome, and 'ee puts it in the pig-sty. When the man gets 'ome, the master asks 'im where was the ship. 'Ee sez: 'I brought it in the yard 'ere', 'ee sez. 'Where, then?' 'I brought it in the yard 'ere.' 'Are you sure?'

'Yes, I'm sure of it, sir.' 'Did you see any man on the road?'
'No, sir, I saw no one.' 'I can't see no ship in the yard 'ere',
'ee sez. 'You're a fine fellow to go to buy a ship, an' to lose it
on the road.'

The master goes to Jack. 'Have you got the ship, Jack?'
'Yes, master,' 'ee sez, ' 'ee's in the pig-sty.' 'Well,' 'ee sez,
'my man's goin' to the same place for another one to-
morrow', 'ee sez, 'and see if you can steal the t'other 'un off
him. and if you don't do that,' 'ee sez, 'Jack, I'll be-behead
you.'

So off this man goes to fetch the ship, but the master didn't
tell the man nothin' about Jack takin' the ship off 'im. So
Jack was settin' down at the end of the wood listenin' for the
ship to come. He 'eared the ship comin' an' the man a-
shoutin' 'Yoop, yooee!' an' the ship went 'Baaaa'. Jack went
'Baaaa' back again in the wood, an' begin to rattle the laves.

An' this man says to 'isself: 'Husht!' 'ee sez, 'Dasht!' 'ee
sez, 'there's that ship I lost last night.' So the ship went
'Baaa', and Jack went 'Baaa' again. 'Eh!' 'ee sez, 'if I catch
that ship', 'ee sez, 'an take it 'ome, wouldn't the master be
very good friends with me again?' So 'ee runs up the wood
after Jack, an' Jack kips runnin' on afore 'im shoutin'
'Baaa'. An' Jack tuk 'im about 'alf a mile up the wood, an'
Jack know'd the near cut to come back, an' come an' tuk the
t'other ship as 'ee'd fastened to the hedge, while 'ee was after
the t'other 'un.

So the man goes 'ome, and the master axed him where was
the ship. So 'ee didn't like to tell 'im as 'ee'd fastened it to
the hedge, while 'ee was after the t'other 'un. An' the master
sez: 'You'm no good to me, losin' my ship: I'll give you the
sack.'

Goes down to Jack, the master did, an' 'ee sez, 'Have you
got the ship, Jack?' 'Ay, master,' 'ee sez, ' 'ee's in the pig-
sty.' 'Well now, Jack,' 'ee sez, 'I'm goin' to put you on to a
hot job, this time', 'ee sez. 'I'm goin' to have twelve soldiers',
'ee sez, 'and all armunition in my room to watch you comin',
and if you can't take the middlemost sheet from underneath
me an' my missus 'ithout them seein' you, I'll be-behead
you.'

Now Jack know'd where there'd bin a young man newly

buried in the churchyard hard by, an' 'ee goes an' gets a
pick an' shovel, and 'ee rises this dead body up. 'Ee goes an'
'ee gets a long ladder, one as reached from the side of the
'ouse to the top of the chimley, an' 'ee gets a piece of rope.
He ties it round this dead man's neck into a slip knot, an' 'ee
loosed 'im down the chimley.

'Husht! he's comin', I can 'ear him', the master sez. He
shouted 'Fire!' and all the men fired. They thought they'd
killed him—the room bein' so dark with the smoke, they
couldn't see what sort of man he was. He sez: 'Thank God!
we've killed 'im. If we hadn't killed 'im, 'ee'd 'ave killed we
in time. Bring 'im along, boys; we'll soon dig a bit of a hole
for 'im somewheres.'

So while they were away burying him Jack goes upstairs
to the missus. 'By gum!' 'ee sez, ' 'tis cowld. Thank God,
we've killed 'im. Lie further.' He got into bed with the
rawnie [lady]. So all the time 'ee got suvin' the rawnie, 'ee
kept drawin' the sheet from under 'er. 'I'll go an' see if
they've buried 'im', 'ee sez. 'By gum! they're a long time
over it.'

Out 'ee goes with the sheet, an' the master comes in, an'
'ee tells 'er to lie further. So the master begins to lel a bit of
minj. 'By gum!' she sez, 'you wants it oftener to-night till
another time. It's not above ten minutes since you had it
afore.' 'I'll bet my life Jack's bin 'ere again', sez the master.

Now we'll lave the master to stand a bit, an' go back to the
mother. So in the morning Jack sez to his mother: 'Mother,'
'ee sez, 'give me one of them owld bladders as hang up in the
house, and', 'ee sez, 'I'll fill it full of blood, an' I'll tie it
round your throat, an' when the master comes up to me to
ax me if I got the sheet, me an' you'll be 'avin' a bit of argle-
ment, an' I'll up with my fist, an' hit you on the bladder, an'
the bladder'll bust, an' you'll make yourself to be dead.'

Now the master comes. 'Have you got the sheet, Jack?'
An' just as he's axin' 'im 'ee ups with his fist, an' hits his
mother. An' the master sez: 'Oh, Jack, what did you kill
your poor mother for?' 'Oh, I don't care, I can soon bring
'er right again.' 'No,' sez the master, 'never, Jack.'

An' Jack begin to smile, an' 'ee sez, 'Can't I? You'll see,
then.' And he goes behind the door, an' fetches a stick with a

bit of a knob to it. Jack begin to laugh. He touches 'is mother with this stick, and the 'owld 'ooman jumped up (This is 'sposed to be an *in*chanted stick.)

Sez the master: 'Oh, Jack,' 'ee sez, 'what shall I give you for that stick?' 'Well, sir,' he sez, 'I couldn't let you 'ave that stick, my inchantment would be broke.' 'Well, Jack, if you'll let me 'ave that stick, I'll never give you another thing to do as long as you live here.' So he give 'im fifty pouns for this stick, and sed 'ee'd never give 'im nothin' else to do for 'im.

So the master went 'ome to the 'ouse, and 'ee didn't know which way to fall out with the missus to try this stick. One day at dinner-time 'ee 'appened to fall out with her: the dinner she put for 'im didn't plase 'im. So 'ee ups with 'is fist, an' 'ee knocks 'er dead. In comes the poor sarvint girl and sez: 'Oh, master, whatever did you kill the poor missus for?' He sez: 'I'll sarve you the same': an' 'ee sarved 'er the same. In comes the wagoner, an' 'ee axed what did 'ee kill the missus and the sarvint for. An' he sez: 'I'll sarve *you* the same', 'ee sez.

He wanted to try the stick what 'ee 'ad off Jack. He thought he could use it the same way as Jack. So he touched the sarvint with it, an' she never rose. He touched the wagoner, an' 'ee never rose. 'Well,' 'ee sez, 'I'll try the big end', 'ee sez, an' 'ee tries the knob. So, 'ee battered and battered with the knob, till 'ee battered the brains out of the three of 'em.

He does no more, and 'ee goes up to Jack, an' sez: 'Oh, Jack, you've ruined me for life.' 'Ee sez: 'Jack, I shall 'ave to drown you.' So Jack sez: 'All right, master.' 'Well, get in this bag', 'ee sez; an' 'ee takes 'im on 'is back. As 'ee was goin' along the road, 'ee took very short, an' went to do a job for 'isself. Him being a very methlyist man, 'ee went one field off the road. During the time 'ee was down there, there come a drovier by with 'is cattle. Now Jack's head was out of the sack.

'Hello, Jack, where are you going?' 'To heaven, I hope.' 'Oh, Jack, let *me* go: I'm an owlder man till you, and I'll give you all my money and this cattle.' Jack told 'im to on-loosen the bag to let 'im out, and for 'im to get into it. Away Jack goes with the cattle and the money.

So the master comes up, taking no notice of it, an' 'ee

picks the bag up an' puts it on 'is shoulder, an' goes on till 'ee comes to Montfort's Bridge. He sez: 'One, two, three', and away 'ee chucks 'im over.

Well, Jack goes now about the country daling in cattle. So in about three years' time he comes round the same way again, round the master's place. So, 'Hello, Jack,' 'ee sez, 'wherever did you get them from?' 'Well, sir,' 'ee sez, 'where you throwed me, if I'd 'ad a little boy at the turnin' to turn 'em straight down the road, I should 'ave 'ad as many more.'

So 'ee sez: 'Jack, will you chuck me there, an' you stop at the turnin' to turn 'em?' So Jack sez: 'You'll 'ave to walk till you get there, for I can't carry you.' And when 'ee got to the bridge, Jack put 'im in the bag, an' Jack counted 'is 'one, two, three', same as 'ee counted for 'im, and away 'ee goes.

And Jack went back an' tuk to the farm, and makin' very good use of it; for a many a night 'ee let me stop in 'is field with my tent for telling you that big lie about 'im.

44. The Tinker's Wife

Once there was a tinker and his wife, and they got into a bit of very good country for yernin' a few shillings quick. And in this country there wasn't very little lodgings. 'Well, my wench,' he said to his wife, 'I think we'll go and take that little empty house, and keep a little beer. Well, my wench, I'll order for a barrel of beer.' He has this barrel of beer in the house. 'Now, my wench, you make the biggest penny out of it as ever you can, and I'll go off for another week's walk.'

In the course of one day a packman come by. He says, 'It's gettin' very warm, missus, isn't it?' 'No, indeed,' she says, 'it's very cold weather.' 'I've got a very big load, and it makes me sweat, and I think it's warm.' 'I sell beer here', she says. He says, 'Well, God bless you, put me a drop for this penny.' It was one of the old big pennies, and was the biggest penny she ever saw there. She brought him all the barrel for it. So she takes the penny and drops it in the basin on the mantel-shelf. He was there three days drinking till he emptied the barrel of beer.

The husband comes home at the end of the week. 'Well, my wench, how did you get on?' 'Well, Jack, I did very well. I sold every drop of beer.' 'Well done, my wench, we'll have another one and see how that goes. Now, my wench, bring them few shillin's down, and let's see what you made upon it.'

She brings the basin down, and says, 'You told me to make the biggest penny on it as ever I could.'

He begin to count it, and turns the basin upside down, and empties it on the table. And what was there but the one big penny? 'Well! ! well! ! well! ! ! !' he says, 'you'll ruin me for life.' 'Ah!' she says, 'Jack, didn't you tell me to make the biggest penny out of it as ever I could, and that was the biggest penny as ever I seen.'

'Well,' he says, 'my wench, I see you don't understand sellin' beer. I think I'll buy a little pig. We've got plenty of taters and cabbage in the garden. Well, now, my wench, when the butcher comes round to kill the pig, you walk round the garden and count every cabbage that's in the garden, and you get a little stick, and stick it by every cabbage in the garden, and when the butcher slays the pig up, you revide a piece of pig up for every cabbage in the garden.' She revided a piece of pig up for every cabbage in the garden, and stuck it on every stick round the cabbages.

The husband comes home again. 'Well, my wife, how did you go on with the pig?' 'Well, Jack, I done as you told me', she says; 'I got a stick and stuck it by every cabbage, and put a piece of mate on every stick.'

'Well! ! well! ! well! ! ! !' he says, 'where is the mate gone to now? You'll ruin me if I stop here much longer. Pull the fire out', he says, 'and I'll get away from here.' And he picks up his basket and throws it on his shoulder. 'Pull that door after you', he says.

What did she do but she pulls all the fire out and put it into her apron. The old door of the house was tumbling down, and she picks it up and put it on her back. So him being into a temper, he didn't take much notice of her behind him. They travelled on, and it comes very dark. They comes to an old hollow tree by the side of the road. 'Well, my wench, I think we'll stop here to-night.'

They goes up to the top of the old tree. After they got up

in the tree, the robbers got underneath them. 'Whatever you do, my wench, keep quiet. This is a robbers' den.' The robbers had plenty of meat and everything, and they prayed for a bit of fire. She says, 'Jack,' she says, 'I shall have to drop it.' So she drops the fire out of her apron, and it goed down the hollow tree. 'See, what a godsend that is', said one.

They cooked the meat as they had. 'The Lord send me a drop of vinegar', says one. . . . All down the hollow tree it dropped. And all the plates being laid out on the ground, a drop fell on each. . . . 'Thank God for that', says that other one, 'see what a godsend 'tis to us.'

Now, the door's fastened to her back yet, and she says, 'Jack, I shall have to drop it.' 'Drop what?' he says. 'I shall have to drop the door, Jack,' she says, 'the rope's cutting my shoulders in two.'

So she drops the door down the hollow tree, and it went dummel-tummel-tummel down the tree, and these robbers thought 'twas the devil himself coming. They jumps up, and away they goes down the road, as hard as ever they could go. The time as they run, Jack's wife goes down the tree and picks up the bag of gold what they'd left. Being frightened as they'd had such godsends to 'em, they left all behind.

They had one brother as was deaf and dumb. Him being a very valuable [valiant] fellow, he thought he'd come back to see what was the matter. He come peepin' round the old tree. Who happened to see him but Jack's wife. And he went 'A-a-a-a-a' to her. 'Come here,' she says, 'I can cure your speech.'

She made motions with her own mouth for him to put his tongue out. She drew the knife slightly from behind her as he put his tongue out, and cut half of his tongue off. Him being bleeding, he went 'Awa-wa-wa-wa,' putting his hand to his mouth and making motions to his brothers. And when he got back to his brothers, them seeing him bleeding, they thought sure the devil was there.

I never see Jack nor his wife nor the robbers sence after they left the tree.